STACK IT!

STACK IT!

The Ultimate New Strategy for Mass!

Robert Kennedy

 Sterling Publishing Co., Inc. **New York**

Designed by *JIM ANDERSON*

Library of Congress Cataloging-in-Publication Data

Kennedy, Robert, 1938—
    Stack it! : the ultimate new strategy for mass! / Robert Kennedy.
       p.   cm.
    Includes index.
    ISBN 0-8069-8292-6
    1. Bodybuilding.   I. Title.
GV546.5.K4629   1991
646.7′5—dc20   91-17610
                                        CIP

10 9 8 7 6 5 4 3 2

© 1991 by Robert Kennedy
Published by Sterling Publishing Company, Inc.
387 Park Avenue South, New York, N.Y. 10016
Distributed in Canada by Sterling Publishing
℅ Canadian Manda Group, P.O. Box 920, Station U
Toronto, Ontario, Canada M8Z 5P9
Distributed in Great Britain and Europe by Cassell PLC
Villiers House, 41/47 Strand, London WC2N 5JE, England
Distributed in Australia by Capricorn Ltd.
P.O. Box 665, Lane Cove, NSW 2066
Manufactured in the United States of America
All rights reserved

Sterling ISBN 0-8069-8292-6

CONTENTS

FOREWORD

What It's All About

Francis Benfatto shows muscular perfection.

Phil Hill

This book is basically an advanced trainer's guide to bodybuilding. As you peruse these pages, you will find sound advice for increasing muscle mass and strength while limiting body fat, regardless of the present condition of your physique. Gaining muscle while losing fat is what it's all about. But it's more than that. It is always my wish that you build muscle proportionately, according to the unique symmetry of your size and shape. My other concerns are that you build your body without injury to your joints and muscles—and that abounding, vigorous health be always part of your goal.

Musclebuilding for both sexes is among the most exciting and rewarding hobbies available. There are other shorter-term pleasures in life that require a lot less time and energy, that are certainly enjoyable and rewarding, but the benefits of bodybuilding are hard to beat. Not only can strenuous training be pleasurable, but we are involving ourselves in the creation of a work of art: the development of our own bodies. As bodybuilders, we are our own sculptors. With the proper use of free-weight training and variable-resistance machines, we can add muscle, take off fat, shape and hone, round out or flatten, carve in cuts, forge striations, build rock hardness, and ultimately change our bodies in any direction we want.

Many people already know the excitement and satisfaction of gaining physical fitness and building a better body. To be in shape, "tight and built," is a joy. It is a special reward when you have done the job yourself with persistent training. Creating a body beautiful out of a poorly conditioned physique can lead to true happiness. Building slabs of muscle on a skinny frame is a road to euphoria. The world is a better place when we are riding the wave of superior health and physical fitness.

Men! Follow the advice in *Stack It!* Learn how you can build muscle and lose fat. Find out how you can create the kind of body that men respect and women admire.

Women! Now you can move into the realm of the truly sensational. A totally toned

Germany's remarkable Anja Langer

body can be yours. And it can be done in less time than you imagine.

It's your move to make it happen. Your ideal body is waiting for you in the mirror. It's just around the corner. Start stacking it!

1
MOTIVATION
Keeping Enthusiasm High

What a back! Laura Creavalle stops for a pose.

Johnny Morant and Robby Robinson

What motivates the champs to attain greatness? It could be a wish to overcome an inferiority complex or an innate drive to appeal to the opposite sex.

Ask ten champion bodybuilders what motivates them, and you may well get ten different answers. Some are motivated to achieve success and recognition that was missing in their formative years. Others received loads of nurturing support and love in their childhood, and realizing a good thing, they want more of the same.

When I first started training in the sixties, I wasn't exactly gung ho on bodybuilding, but after a few weeks of performing chin-ups and push-ups and working out with some weights I found around the house, I noticed some muscle growth. I can still remember my initial shock. "Hey! This stuff works." That in itself was reason enough to train. It's true that nothing enthuses and motivates us more than seeing progress.

What got you into regular training? Many experienced that initial impetus after seeing a bodybuilding magazine or a well-built person in a movie or at the beach. It's wonderful when we are totally motivated—when our natural enthusiasm inspires us to go to the gym. But time has a way of dampening enthusiasm. If you don't have that natural drive and determination to excel, you have to drum it up. You must have a clear goal that will get you past any second thoughts you may have about training day after day, eating frequent, musclebuilding meals, and supplementing for additional mass.

Arnold Schwarzenegger said, "Without a firm goal in mind, you may wonder why you're torturing yourself in the gym day after day."

Accept challenges. Do you have an underdeveloped body part? Are you weak at a certain exercise? Decide to change things around and then go for it. Strive for improvement with 100 percent motivation. You *will* beat the problem. You *will* build those arms. You *will* become a champion. Remember, if you want something badly enough, you will get it. When athletes have something to aim for—something in their sights—they always achieve greatness.

The inimitable Cory Everson

Holland's Berry DeMey is spotted by his brother for a set of curls.

Motivation can be kept very much alive by training with a workout partner. Choose someone who will encourage you to attain your goal. You don't want a shouter who screams at you to perform another rep. He's just trying to draw attention to himself. It's far better that your training partner gives you soft-spoken encouragement: "Two more reps . . . come on, you can do it!" Training partners can push each other to exercise harder and more consistently. There's a friendly competition, and you tend to rest less when training with a friend.

I well remember a training partner that Lou Ferrigno had a dozen years ago. The guy would shout so loudly that even Lou took off his hearing aid. I also remember that Arnold Schwarzenegger said to Lou after the gym members had endured this partner for several weeks: "Louie, get rid of the training partner. He's not helping things." Soon afterward, the Hulk had acquired a far more considerate training buddy, and his muscles started growing again.

Another way to keep motivation high is to add variety to your training. It's easy to get into a rut in bodybuilding. Following the same old exercises day after day can be boring, especially if you have come to a sticking point. One professional bodybuilder told me that he had always performed the same workout for his thighs. He did ten sets of twelve reps of heavy squats, moved onto the hack machine, and then performed leg curls. He confided to me that he dreaded his leg-workout day and almost got sick the night before, worrying about the heavy squats he'd have to do. He could have taken some of the pain out of his training by alleviating the boredom. Although sets of back squats are hard to beat, there's no reason not to change things around a bit. A period of performing low-rep squats (say, five sets of six reps) followed by five sets of fifteen reps on the hack machine or thigh extensions could make a welcome change while still encouraging development. Actually, squats can be eliminated altogether. Substitute leg presses in the inverted position or the 45-degree variety. Another variation is to pre-exhaust the quadriceps by alternating sets of thigh extensions with squat or hack exercises.

"One more rep!" Shawn Ray tells Troy Zuccolotto.

Check out the amazing biceps peak on Ronald Matz.

Peter Potter, the National Physique Committee vice-president, conducted a survey on women's bodybuilding to find out the various motivations for training. Here's how the motivation factor influenced the reasons for working out:

1. Improve overall appearance (33.9 percent)
2. Increase self-confidence (15.7 percent)
3. Lose weight and firm up (13 percent)
4. Aid athletic performance (10.4 percent)
5. Influence of trainer (6.5 percent)
6. Encouragement from husband/boyfriend (6.5 percent)
7. Rehabilitation from accident/injury (3.8 percent)
8. Increase strength (2.6 percent)
9. Love of competition (2.6 percent)
10. Influence of gym owner (1.2 percent)

Fully one third of the women who were surveyed train to improve their appearance. This is the key to maintaining a high degree of motivation—the desire to look great!

For the most part, bodybuilders at all levels do feel better about their appearance when they train, which results in added muscle, improved posture, and a well-toned condition. There's no doubt about it: Bodybuilders are proud of their bodies. I don't mean to suggest that a bodybuilder is superior to anyone else, nor is he or she superior physically to a trained athlete, for example. But training for a strong and conditioned body does make you proud of your appearance. You radiate self-confidence. All this motivates you to maintain what you have built.

True bodybuilders never stop training. They want to keep their optimal physical condition for as long as possible. Recently I was with Steve Reeves and Reg Park, each of whom is well into his sixties, but each is still training and looking vital, fit, healthy and amazingly well built. Their motivation has always been improved fitness and appearance. Keep this factor in mind for yourself and your enthusiasm and motivation will never wane.

Cameo Kneuer is Cory Everson's "little" sister.

2 BODY RESTORATION
Cellular Recovery

Francis Benfatto begins his posing routine.

Laura Creavalle works her arms on the cable machine.

I have been criticized many times for suggesting that in bodybuilding, as well as in most sports, "More *is* better." I still believe this to be true in the case of those wishing to excel in international competition. Let's face it: You're not going to be a Mr. or Ms. Olympia while training Mondays, Wednesdays, and Fridays for 45-minute workouts. Neither will you find someone who builds 20-inch arms with three sets of exercises for the triceps and biceps. All the champs of bodybuilding have won their titles by performing *lots of sets and reps.*

It's true that performing three or four half-hour workouts a week will build you a muscular body, but building a *massive* muscular body requires more time in the gym. You have to push your muscles right to the edge of progressive-resistance training to become a champion. It's quite within the bounds of reason for a man to develop a 17-inch arm by training six to eight exercise sets per body part, but to get those extra two or three inches to put him into the winner's circle may take considerably more time and effort. Frequently, to obtain just 5 percent more muscle mass, you have to increase your workout output by an additional 20 percent. Champions like Cory Everson, Lee Haney, Frank Zane, Rich Gaspari, Berry DeMey, Gary Strydom, and the incredible Arnold Schwarzenegger all performed long hours of repetitive training. Why? Because they wanted that extra pound of muscle for the competitive edge.

I'm convinced that to reach the top in any sporting event, more *is* better. There's one proviso, of course. We have to be able to recover from our workouts. Dr. Fred Hatfield, who claims that overtraining is the most common problem among athletes today, says, "There's just no shortcut to proper training. No matter what your sport, you improve by cooperating with your body's own cycles of work and recovery, or destruction and regeneration of muscle tissue."

Dr. Ellington Darden contends, "Muscle cell injury, not growth, remains the only direct result from exercise. Muscular growth comes from your recovery processes."

Recuperation is dependent on getting adequate rest, balanced nutrition, and sufficient

Rich Gaspari pumps up with cable curls.

The master of mass—Gary Strydom

recovery time between workouts. How does recuperation work? Initially, after a workout, the body attempts to recover energy lost during the training session. Then the musclebuilding process will follow, but only if the muscles have been stimulated sufficiently to cause additional growth. Too many or too long workouts will tend to prevent gains in muscle growth because all the recovery time will have gone into overcoming the exhaustive effects of the workout.

Fred Howell, a writer for the bodybuilding press, claims, "The less you train the more you gain." Dr. Darden also has written: "The facts strongly suggest that the less time you spend in the gym the better." I certainly can't agree with either of these statements. To gain large, round muscles, you have to train creatively. You have to coax, shock, and pound your muscles to stimulate development. You have to pay your dues in the gym with lots of sets and reps. And then you have to recover from your workouts as quickly as possible. How do you recover in the quickest-possible time?

Adequate Rest

To some bodybuilders, rest means that period when they are not training. But at least a portion of your resting time should be *quality* rest, such as lying in a hot tub, enjoying a massage, relaxing in a chair, lying on a couch, watching television, or reading a book. Walking around an office, performing manual work, or engaging in any other taxing activity where you are constantly on the go is not quality rest.

According to Stephen Kiesling, the author of *Loafing: Secret of Champions*, "Rest isn't just a matter of making yourself feel better; it's essential to the very cells of your body. Researchers who examined leg-muscle cells of athletes saw twisted cells, torn cells, and cells turned inside out." This prompted researchers to conclude that many athletes were drastically overtraining without getting enough rest. How much rest is too much? Resting more than 72 hours between workouts would probably hold back progress substantially.

Krista and Dinah Anderson compare biceps.

Sunshine and Fresh Air

Sunshine is getting a bad rap nowadays from all the worry about skin damage caused by ultraviolet radiation. In reality, the sun is essential for the continuation of life itself. Small to moderate amounts of sunshine will help increase testosterone levels, induce chemical repair mechanisms, and generally aid recuperation in the body. Of course, excessive amounts of sunshine will inhibit the recovery process. You will be drained of vitality and have zero energy. Too much exposure to the sun, especially if taken to the burning stage, will induce blistering, peeling, and permanent skin damage. Even skin cancer can result from excessive sun exposure. Always protect your skin from the sun by wearing a sunscreen that blocks the damaging ultraviolet rays.

Recuperation is also aided by getting out in the fresh air. Oxygen is known to regenerate the blood and supply the cells with energy, which helps the cells recover from strenuous exercise.

Balanced Diet

I have written extensively about diet in Chapter 12: Bodybuilding Nutrition, but it goes without saying that when a muscle cell is broken down through strenuous progressive-resistance exercise, it must be adequately nourished to allow it to develop. Complex carbohydrates and proteins will serve to build up muscle mass, while vitamins and minerals are the micronutrients required for a perfectly functioning and healthy physique. Keep your nutrition levels well balanced with unprocessed foods in their natural state.

Debbie Kruck

The Muscle Sleep

We all have to work for a living. And curiously enough, many bodybuilders actually work at two jobs because they want extra cash for vitamins and supplements. But getting sufficient sleep is vital for hard trainers. There is no doubt that many competitive physique men and women do sleep for an hour or two during the day. It's called the "muscle sleep." Some bodybuilders keep this siesta to 40 minutes, while others will sleep for two hours or so. Muscle sleeps are most effective when you are training twice a day for an upcoming competition.

"I feel that a muscle sleep is vital if we are to achieve our maximum potential," says Albert Beckles, who has taken a short snooze after his morning workout for the last thirty years.

Of course, there are many professional bodybuilders who do not sleep at all during the day, but I have found that up to 40 percent do. They claim it to be a very worthwhile habit when it comes to helping the body to recover.

Energy Conservation

One of my favorite writers on matters of muscle was John Barrs, an Englishman who wrote extensively on bodybuilding way back in the forties. John wrote, "You want muscle? Then equally important as diet and training is the conservation of energy. It is of no use to punch holes in the bottom of a bucket you wish to fill. An enemy to weight gaining is excessive exercise, the practice of sports and games in addition to regular free-weight workouts."

The trainer who is following a scientific program to build muscle mass, who continues to play tennis or football, or to practice karate or gymnastics as well, is merely delaying his progress.

Mental Relaxation

"Next time you go outside, look at the people you meet. Note the poor posture, observe the blank faces, look at the tension and worry in their faces," writes Dr. Fred Tilney of Florida. Hurrying and worrying are just as destructive to muscle development as lack of sleep or overactivity. You must plan your life to reduce these negative elements to a minimum. It is better to get up in the morning a half hour earlier than to have to make up for lost time by rushing through breakfast and dashing to work.

Mental frustration and worry over lack of bodybuilding gains will feed on itself, and your sticking point will deepen. I am all for you reading as much as you can on the subject of bodybuilding, but take pleasure in other subjects, too. If you can choose a time to read up on bodybuilding, do it just before a workout. You'll get fired up like crazy. But getting your adrenaline pumping at night before you go to sleep may not be such a great idea. Nighttime is when you want your body to shut down and relax. You don't need a thumping heart and pumping adrenaline to interrupt or curtail your sleep.

After your workout, avoid feeling anxious by encouraging your mind to unwind. Put your feet up, sip a protein drink, and relax. Calm down, slow down, and watch those muscles grow.

Overtraining

One secret of being able to continue your muscle gains is to conquer your desire to train too much, causing an overtraining slump to set in. By all means, make sure that your gym time is spent with quality training, but there will seldom be a need to train for more than two hours at a time. In fact, many bodybuilders do well by limiting their workouts to 60 to 90 minutes. Remember, if you drain your energy and physical resources in the gym, you will have nothing left for growth. Work hard to stimulate growth, but not so hard or long that you disrupt your body chemistry to the extent of requiring excessive sleep and rest for recovery.

Don't allow any obsessions to undermine your chosen goals. Bodybuilding is a wonderful sport. By performing sensible and regular workouts, you are sure to accomplish your dreams.

Sandy Riddell curls with the rotating-grip barbell.

3
OPTIMAL
HEALTH
Robust
Well-Being

Australia's John Terilli sports massive double biceps.

Alternate dumbbell curls by Debbie Kruck, Ms. Fitness U.S.A.

Doctors often interpret being healthy as being free from disease. Many cigarette smokers have been given first-rate health assessments by their family doctors. How often have you heard of individuals who have keeled over with heart attacks within weeks of being examined by a doctor and said to possess excellent health? Were they *really* in good condition when they were diagnosed?

Health is a vast and complex subject whose basis lies in genetics. We have a good chance of maintaining top health if we have inherited vigorous good health from our forebears. Alternatively, if we have some of the scores of disorders in our family history, then our luck of the draw is less than perfect for optimal health.

Whatever the case, whether we have strong or weak genetics, we must guard our health by following sensible life-styles. It has been said that the healthiest people are those who never think about health. I must admit that I have had many conversations with people who could only be regarded as "health nuts." In spite of their high interest in wellness, many of these people were actually very troubled, stressed, and unhealthy. In their quest for perfect health, their enthusiasm had turned into fanaticism.

Take the strict vegetarian, for example— the person who eats no dairy or animal products whatsoever. Qualified nutritionists will tell you that the diet is inadequate to support perpetual high-grade wellness.

Look at the fanatical marathon runners who run their bodies into the ground all in the name of health. Many of them end up with foot and joint injuries that plague their middle and advanced years, not to mention the pounding they give their muscle cells, electrolyte balance, and cooling mechanisms.

And then there are the food fanatics. Many people have made themselves sick by eating an overabundance of products made from roots, herbs, berries, and "natural" concoctions that left them with a case of malnutrition. Remember that even water or oxygen in excess can make you sick.

Exercise

Ostensibly all sports will improve your physical fitness if they challenge your aerobic condition. But today, with the enormous pressure to win, most sports played at the competition level are *not* conducive to good health. Football, hockey, and other contact sports cause all kinds of tendon, joint, and muscle injuries. Weightlifters and powerlifters subject their joints to excessive stress. Boxers knock each other senseless ... and the list goes on.

Exercise in moderation is the answer—swimming, racketball, volleyball, tennis, cycling, and walking. Although aerobic dance, stair climbing, rope jumping, stationary bike and stair machine exercises can all be very healthful, always remember to do them at least two or three times a week, and exercise according to your current state of fitness. Never overdo it! Be sensible. All new exercise programs have to be started with minimal exertion initially. Systematic exercise raises the heart rate and expands the lungs for an improved cardiovascular function. It lowers blood pressure, burns calories, and reduces body-fat levels. You will also feel better after your workouts, because exercise reduces stress levels.

Stretching is also a healthful activity that keeps you flexible and free from injury. Keep those joints and tendons strong. Stretching is a simple way to keep your body lithe, supple and physically toned. A stretching session before or after your workout may take a few extra minutes, but the results are worth it.

Optimal Nutrition

Western society has made many advances over the years, but nutrition isn't one of them. Most people eat too much animal fat, excessive amounts of salt, and too many sugar-loaded products.

"We need to return to the caveman's diet: three-quarters fruits, vegetables, and whole grains, and one-quarter fish or lean meat. Include no table salt, or sugar," says veteran trainer Vince Gironda.

Robert Augustin

John Hnatyshack performs a dumbbell wrist curl.

Fresh produce is best because processing removes essential vitamins and minerals. Eat your fruits and vegetables raw if possible, or steam or bake them. Meats and fish should be baked or broiled. Eat no fried foods whatsoever. Cut down on regular cheese, cream, sauces, yogurt, whole milk, and butter, and substitute low-fat equivalents for them.

Don't underestimate the importance of potassium-rich foods such as bananas, potatoes, lima beans, orange juice, yellow squash, broccoli, spinach, sunflower seeds, and peanuts. "High-potassium diets," says health expert Michael Kedo, "prevent closure of arteries and may be a positive influence in minimizing high-cholesterol conditions and even some cancers."

Hardworking bodybuilders must consume enough potassium to replace what they lose through sweating. By drinking a reputable electrolyte-replacement fluid after training, you will help maintain a correct potassium level.

Stress Reduction

Reduce the stress in your life to a manageable level. Excessive worrying can cause secretions of adrenaline, the "fight-or-flight" hormone. The response is not dissimilar to being in a dark forest at night and hearing footsteps behind you. Your body expects to perform intense physical activity and starts to pump adrenaline, increasing your heart rate and blood pressure. Repeated stresses can cause this situation to occur throughout the day. In time, you could suffer arterial shutdown, and possibly angina symptoms, ulcers, or other stress-related diseases.

Learn to relax. Go for a walk and breath the fresh air. Get a massage or soak in a hot tub. Forget about gnawing obligations or job-related worries. Accept the joys of life outside your immediate problems.

Healthful Habits

They say a good habit is as easy to form as a bad one. Then why do people enjoy eating junk food, drinking alcohol and coffee, and smoking cigarettes?

Realistically, we all have a tendency to adopt at least one bad habit. Let's not be too fanatical. Having an occasional drink is acceptable. Drinking up to three cups of coffee a day is reportedly not excessive. Smoking, however, should be curtailed entirely. Researchers have found that cigarette smoking causes arterial spasms that narrow the blood vessels. It also accelerates fatty buildup in the arteries, causing platelets in the bloodstream to clump together. You cannot be vigorous and healthy if you are a heavy smoker. The same, of course, goes for taking recreational drugs.

Cleanliness goes hand in hand with good health. Wash your hands and face frequently, and take a daily shower.

Medical Check-Ups

Get regular checkups with your doctor so that any medical problems that arise can be attended to as soon as possible. This is especially true if you have a specific condition that requires monitoring.

See your dentist twice a year and get immediate attention for any loose fillings, broken teeth, or other dental problems.

If you have reason to believe that your eyesight is less than perfect, then see an optician and get fitted with suitable corrective lenses. This is particularly important if you are approaching middle age.

Self-Awareness

Become aware of how you feel and how your body functions. Without becoming a hypochondriac, it's a good idea to be in touch with your body and mind. See your doctor if you have regular chest or stomach pain. Long bouts of constipation or diarrhea should also be checked, along with spells of hot flashes, dizziness, or faintness. We all suffer small aches and pains, which are part of life, but regular pain or discomfort is the body's way of indicating something is not quite right. See your physician. Chances are, nothing is wrong that can't be easily treated, but the sooner you see your doctor, the quicker your total recovery will be.

4

WORKOUT FREQUENCY
When
to Train

Canada's Nimrod King watches his biceps during a concentration curl.

Aaron Baker shows mass in a pensive mood.

Beginning bodybuilders are always contemplating the importance of sets and reps, yet few bother to give much thought to workout frequency. Later on, during the intermediate and advanced stages, as workouts tend to get longer, more tiring, and harder to recover from, we direct our attention to frequency. Am I training too hard or not enough? How much rest do I need? How many times a week should I train?

Mike Mentzer, the Mr. Universe with a perfect score, says, "Why limit yourself to fitting workouts into an odd number of days?" True enough, many of us work from Monday to Friday, and like to keep the weekend free to spend with family and friends. In this case, design your workout frequency to fit your situation. There are many frequency patterns that allow us to keep Saturdays and Sundays free for other interests.

How many times a week we train is not as important as how frequently we should train each body part. There has to be some leeway here. Why? Because some of us are fitter, younger, stronger, and more suited to the rigors of strenuous exercise than others. When I was young and beginning in this sport, I trained all body parts on a full routine six days a week. I loved it, never tired, never got sick, but never grew! I also knew people who only did a dozen workouts a year. (They didn't grow either!)

Today, I realize that workout-frequency patterns are extremely important. And I have come to some conclusions.

Frequency Conclusion Number One
Off-season trainers wishing to gain maximum muscle mass in the shortest period of time should train each body part once every three or four days.

Frequency Conclusion Number Two
Bodybuilders preparing for a contest should spend the last four to ten weeks training each body part once every two or three days.

How do my suggestions relate to the man-made workout? Well, off-season trainers should work each body part twice weekly. Those who are fine-tuning for a contest should train each

Vince Comerford and Dean Tornabean

area three times a week, but always keep aware that you don't overtrain. When you exercise each area as frequently as this, and especially if you are limiting your calorie intake, there is a very real danger of overtraining. In that case, you may have to decrease your frequency schedule.

Bear in mind that progressive-resistance bodybuilding with weights is the most demanding system known of overloading the muscles. Your muscles require time for recuperation—usually 48 to 72 hours—but this doesn't mean that your workouts have to be spaced 48 to 72

hours apart. However, you shouldn't work the same body part within that time span.

Splitting your routine into two or three parts is the answer, performing one part one day and other areas at other times, and so on. When you split your routine, you can work out two or more days in succession, because you are not working the same body part two days in a row. One day you may work your chest, back, and biceps, while the next day's workout could be devoted to shoulders, legs, and triceps. Let's take a closer look at the various frequency patterns.

The Every-Other-Day Split Routine

Are you the type who easily overtrains? Do you feel so stressed from a workout that you can't find the energy to train the next day? If so, this system is for you. Thousands of bodybuilders have used it with success. It's a super way to build size in the off-season period.

Simply split your workout into two parts. Perform the first half of your routine on day one, rest the following day, and then perform the second half of your routine on day three. Rest again the next day, and then start with the first half of your routine on day five. This system is one in which you train every other day, with in-between rest days. You *never* train two days in a row. Why is this such a great system? It allows for

Negrita Jayde

high-intensity training and virtually guarantees full recovery between workouts. Note: Your rest between workouts is *one* day. Never rest for two days in a row. If this happens, you should make up for the missed day by training two days in a row, but don't make this a habit.

The Four-Day Split Routine

The four-day split is another very workable off-season training method. It's popular because it can be arranged to fit within the confines of your work week, thus allowing you to have weekends free.

Divide your workout into two halves, which can be done in several ways. Either divide your exercises into upper and lower body movements, or else split your workout into all *pulling* movements (rows, curls, chin-ups, etc.) on day one, and all *pushing* movements (presses, triceps stretches, squats, etc.) on day two. Actually, all muscles pull, not push, but they *appear* to push when you lift away from the body.

Once split into two parts, perform the first part on Monday and the second part on Tuesday. Wednesday is a rest day. You perform the initial half again on Thursday and the second half on Friday. Presto! The weekends are left free, and you have worked each body part twice weekly, an ideal frequency for maximum muscle growth.

The Monday-Wednesday-Friday Routine

This is a popular method for many, especially beginners and busy people who can only find three days during the work week to train (and who also wish to keep the weekends for other activities). You train your entire body each workout. Naturally, because of the time factor, you will not be able to perform a large number of exercises or sets for each body part. In time, it's likely that you will want to perform more exercises and sets. In order to accommodate more work per body part, you will have to divide your workout into two or three parts and follow another form of workout frequency.

The Six-Day Split Routine

You only get one rest day a week with this method. Each body part is trained three times a week. This schedule may be too much for continued growth, but there is little doubt that the six-day split routine is very workable for those preparing for a contest. Divide your routine into three parts. Perform part one on Monday, part two on Tuesday, and part three on Wednesday. Then do part one again on Thursday, part two on Friday, and part three on Saturday. Sunday is your one and only rest day.

The Two-Days-On/ One-Day-Off Routine

Divide your exercise routine into two roughly equal parts. Work out using the first half on day one; then train the second half of your routine on day two. The next day is a rest day. On day four, begin again with the first part of your routine, following the next day with the second part. Day six is a rest day again.

The two-days-on/one-day-off routine doesn't give you the weekend free. If that's not a problem, it can be a very useful and result-producing system. Naturally, since you work out two days in a row, you should split your routine in such a way that you do not exercise the same body parts two days in a row. Divide your routine so that different areas of the body are worked on successive days. Of course, there will always be some slight overlapping of exercised muscles, since all our muscles are stimulated to some extent whenever we work out. Many trainers like to work the chest, back, and arms on day one, and the shoulders, legs, and abs on day two.

The fabulous Eddie Robinson of Florida

The Three-Day Split Routine

This is the most popular method among competitive bodybuilders. In this case, you divide the routine into three parts. This allows for more sets and a greater variety of movements for each body area. You "hit" your muscles harder and longer, and still manage to train your entire body twice a week. Perform the first third of your workout on day one, work the second third on day two, and the final third on day three. Day four is a rest day. On day five, begin all over again.

It should be pointed out that this method of workout frequency can be demanding. You have to be pretty fit to keep up with it. Ironically, many bodybuilders keep to this method both in off-season and in pre-contest training. The only changes are in diet. Of course, there is an attempt to increase intensity and sometimes repetition counts as the contest date approaches.

5
MASS
BUILDING
Making Massive Muscles

26

Dorian Yates of the United Kingdom

Olympia time with Laura Creavalle

Whether you watch training videos or read the various muscle magazines, learning how to gain muscle mass may appear to be a very complicated issue. The basis of adding size, however, is simplicity itself. But in order to shape an aesthetically pleasing physique, you must follow certain rules of building proportion, detail, and definition.

Like it or not, your overall ability to build *monumental* size is dependent on factors mostly beyond your control. These factors include age, hormone levels, and genetically endowed amounts of muscle cells. "Evidence indicates that very muscular people tend to have more muscle fibres than less muscular people," says Dr. Eric Sternlicht.

And there is precious little evidence to show that muscles hypertrophy by an increase in the number of muscle fibres (hyperplasia). The concept of hyperplasia as a workable phenomenon is the one hope of the bodybuilder who must work hard for every ounce of muscle. The overwhelming evidence shows that however we supplement our diet, whatever we eat, and no matter how hard we train, we are destined to have the same number of muscle cells from the day we are born to the day we die. All we can do is enlarge or plump up each cell by training regularly and eating correctly. The myofibrils within each fibre increase in number. The overall result is larger muscles. However, when we cease training, our muscles will lose some of their mass.

In terms of maximizing muscle mass, fibre type plays an important part. The so-called *fast-twitch* fibres are larger than *slow-twitch* fibres. A bodybuilder with more fast-twitch muscles will therefore have larger muscles. Don't despair, however, if you have a predominance of slow-twitch fibres. Simply focus on high-intensity, high-repetition training. Alternatively, high-intensity, low-repetition training is best for fast-twitch muscle fibre growth.

Training for mass doesn't mean trying to see how much weight you can squat or bench-press. When you work out to build size, you have to bring the muscle into the picture. You aren't trying to heave a weight from point A to point B. Your job is to pulverize and exhaust your muscles with quality work that forces the recovering cells to grow. For example, if you performed several sets of floor dips during every chest workout, you would not build an Olympian-size chest, even if you took each set to failure point. You would get a moderate pump from the exercise, but beyond developing some pectoral shape, the effort would bring few results. On the other hand, doing several sets of bench presses followed by several more sets of dumbbell flyes would give you substantial gains. And if you make each week's workout a little more "progressive," by adding a small amount of weight, then your chest will continue to develop mass.

Mass-building workouts must exhaust the muscles, not the tendons or joints, and certainly not the nervous system. The number of repetitions performed should generally be limited to eight to fifteen. That isn't to say you shouldn't follow the high-rep system now and again. After all, Cory Everson, Tom Platz, and Al Beckles have all used high-rep routines for building mass with great success.

Very low reps with a lot of weight can put too much pressure on the joints. This is not often a problem with multi-joint exercises like bench presses, rows, and squats. Using super-heavy weights for triceps exercises, ab work, incline curls and presses, and forearm and even biceps training is to invite trouble.

Let me tell you a little story. As a 16-year-old kid growing up in Norfolk, England, my parents were very much against my weight training. Even so, I made a crude barbell out of plaster of Paris and biscuit tins, using a rusty iron bar I had found in a field. It weighed 168 pounds. For a long time, I did my shoulder presses, bench presses, rows, squats, and calf work using this bar, but I also used it for curls. As a gawky, skinny kid, it was too much weight for me ... but I curled it anyway. I managed only one, two, or three reps ... *never* more. And as a result, I damaged my elbows to the extent that I had to have surgery to correct the injury.

Even now I could list scores of top bodybuilders who have trained using weight that was

Sensational Shawn Ray

Dorian Yates

the hardcore bodybuilder will be breaking down more and more fibres. Volume training does indeed build bigger muscles.

But don't get the impression that I am against using high-intensity training. My only concern at this moment is to give you all the facts. Bear in mind that I have trained with, and observed the training of, hundreds of bodybuilding champions over the last thirty years. Let's examine each mass-building technique.

Exercise Form

Mike Christian says, "We must train as heavy as possible with perfect exercise form with reps from six to eight per set."

Lee Haney adds, "You should train with a strict exercise style—no cheating."

Bertil Fox states, "Keep piling on the plates, but do your exercises in strict form to avoid injuries and overtraining."

Well, these champions may *say* that strict training is the way to go, but they sure don't follow their own advice. (Check their exercise videos if you doubt my words.) In fact, only the smallest percentage of successful bodybuilders (less than one percent!) actually train strictly. *Virtually all of them use body leverage and momentum and arching, dipping, and swinging movements to perform their repetitions.* And they are right! (To be fair, few of the champs actually bounce out of their squats or jettison the bar off their chests—both potentially dangerous habits—but they do use moderately loose exercise form in most of their exercises.)

Occasionally, the champion feels the need to train strictly, so you will see a super-strict concentration curl or triceps extension, but for every time you observe this, you will notice a dozen instances where the champion is using body momentum to perform his or her reps. So if the big question in your mind is: Which is best—strict or loose training? The answer is: Use both. Mix it up, but be creative. Some exercises must be performed strictly, such as squats. Others like barbell curls, lat pulldowns, and the various rowing motions lend themselves to a looser exercise style.

too heavy for their joints to manage safely. It's no secret that Cory Everson, Arnold Schwarzenegger, Steve Reeves, and Frank Zane have all suffered shoulder problems from doing incline presses with too much weight.

Many times you will read that the only way to build muscle mass is to increase workout intensity. That means you either have to increase the weight while performing the same number of reps, or increase the reps while using the same amount of weight. The high-intensity advocates also stress that performing multiple sets is *not* increasing intensity. Strictly speaking, this may be true, but with each successive set,

Intensity

Make high-intensity exercise work for you by employing it occasionally. You *cannot* make steady increases by employing 100 percent intensity in all your exercise sets. Your nervous system will not take it. And you cannot make it by performing only one or two sets per exercise. However hard you train, one or two sets is not enough to grow muscle mass.

If there is one common similarity among successful bodybuilders, it is this: *They use moderate weights and they perform lots of sets and reps.*

Superheavy efforts with low reps should only be attempted now and again when the muscles would benefit from some heavy work. For example, a bodybuilder may be performing six sets of 10 to 15 reps when bench-pressing. But one day he may feel the need to train heavier, working up to near-limit poundage for just a couple of reps, or even a single attempt with all-out intensity. This happens with bench work, squats, and deadlifts more than other exercises. However, the rule of thumb remains: *lots of sets and reps with moderate poundage.* This doesn't mean that you use the same weights day in and day out. You do have to try and increase resistance, but keep the increments low. Coax your muscles into growth rather than force them into stagnation or injury.

Nutrition

Listen to the advice of Dr. Frederick Hatfield: "Scientific training plus carefully controlled supplementing and diet equal improved nutrient utilization and tissue recuperation for elevated anabolism that leads to greater mass."

Good nutrition is an essential key to gaining muscle mass. To quote Hatfield one more time: "What you eat is what you flex." For building mass, you should eat plenty of complex carbohydrates, such as corn, rice, potatoes, whole-grain flour, breads and cereals, beans, and peas. Make sure you consume lots of fruits and vegetables. Eat a high-protein food with every meal (milk, eggs, meat, poultry, fish, sea-food, cheese, or yogurt). If you are inclined to be overweight, limit your fat intake and substitute low-fat dairy products.

Eat five or six small meals each day rather than overload your digestive system with two hefty meals that will tend to interfere with your regular training schedule.

Thin men and women can drink a protein drink before retiring at night. Try blending a milk-and-egg-protein powder supplement with a banana in milk. (An optimal bodybuilding diet is discussed in detail in Chapter 12.)

Mass-Building Exercises

Emphasize basic multi-joint movements such as bench presses, squats, rows, chin-ups and dips. Train each body part twice a week (or slightly less) and split your routine into two or three sections. (See Chapter 4 on workout frequency.)

Sandy Riddell stopping at the squat midpoint in perfect form.

Dorothy Herndon demonstrates the T-bar row.

Mass-building routines should not be long and drawn out, but don't neglect any body parts. All the muscles should be stimulated, without emphasizing isolation movements (single-joint exercises). Small body parts should be trained to keep them in line with your other muscles. The following are what I consider to be the 25 best mass-building exercises:

Quadriceps (Front Thighs)
Squat
Hack Slide
Leg Press

Leg Biceps
Hamstring Curl

Back
Deadlift
T-bar Row
Chin-up Behind Neck
Lat Machine Pulldown

Chest
Bench Press
Incline Bench Press
Incline Dumbbell Flye
Flat-bench Dumbbell Flye

Shoulder
Press Behind Neck
Upright Row
Seated Alternate Dumbbell Press
Bent-over Dumbbell Lateral Raise

Biceps
Barbell Curl
Incline Dumbbell Curl
Seated Alternate Dumbbell Curl

Triceps
Close-grip EZ-bar Bench Press
Lying Triceps Extension
Parallel Bar Dip

Forearms
Seated Wrist Curl

Calves
Standing Calf Machine Heel Raise

Abdominals
Crunch

John Terilli begins the press-behind-neck for his shoulders.

Principles for Mass Training

Years ago, bodybuilding was a far more hit-or-miss sport than it is today. Whereas one can never guarantee 20-inch arms and 50-inch chests, we know more about what works today than ever before. Prior to the 1950s, most bodybuilders merely lifted weights three times a week and hoped for the best. It's not that they had the wrong system; they didn't have a system!

Pyramiding

Probably the best way to train for mass is to pyramid the weights. That means you add weight after each set while you decrease repetitions. Quite frankly, the pyramid system should *always* be used in heavy exercises like the press behind neck, squats, bench presses, incline presses, and deadlifts. Older bodybuilders should pyramid every exercise whether it is light or heavy.

How does pyramiding work? Here's Mike Christian's suggestion for using the technique for squats.

Sets	Reps	% of Max	Poundage
1	12	50	225
2	10	65	275
3	8	75	315
4	6	85	345
5	6	85	345
6	6	85	345

It's recommended that you finish each pyramid with one set of high reps to blast out a pump. In the example, you might drop the weight to 250 pounds and do 15 to 20 squats to fully exhaust the quads.

Rest-Pause Training

This is a very severe form of working the muscles—definitely not for the faint-hearted. Rest-pause training allows you to use very heavy

Britain's Bertil Fox performs the single-arm row.

weights for a number of repetitions. With maximum poundage, you will manage only one, two, or possibly three reps. But, when you take a brief rest-pause of 30 to 50 seconds, your muscles recover enough to allow you to force out another couple of reps. And if you take a second or even a third rest-pause, you can grind out a set of seven to eight heavy reps. Don't allow your pauses to exceed one minute, because you will lose the essence of the principle if you rest too long between efforts. Use this technique only on one exercise per workout, and limit it to just one rest-pause set. You certainly won't gain muscle size if you try to use the rest-pause method on every exercise.

Straight Sets

Straight sets are still the most popular method of building mass, and bodybuilders all over the world perform them with a high degree of success. Simply perform one set of eight to twelve reps; then rest for one, two or three minutes. Perform another set, followed again by a rest, and then yet another set. Top trainers do four to eight sets per exercise. After you have completed your last set of an exercise and have finished working a particular body part, you may rest for five to ten minutes before going on to attack another body part.

Mass-Building Routines

Beginner

	Sets	Reps
Squat	1–2	12
Hamstring Curl	1–2	15
Bench Press	3	10
T-bar Row	2	10
Press Behind Neck	2	10
Barbell Curl	2	12
Parallel Bar Dip	2	10–15
Standing Calf Raise	2	15–25
Crunch	1	25

Intermediate

	Sets	Reps
Squat	4	12
Leg Press	3	12–15
Hamstring Curl	4	12
T-bar Row	4	12
Chin-up Behind Neck	4	12–15
Bench Press	5	8–12
Incline Dumbbell Flye	3	12
Standing Calf Raise	4	15–25
Press Behind Neck	4	8–10
Bent-over Lateral Raise	4	12
Barbell Curl	4	8–12
Lying Triceps Extension	4	10–12
Crunch	3	25

Advanced

	Sets	Reps
Press Behind Neck	5	8–10
Upright Row	4	10–12
Bent-over Dumbbell Lateral Raise	4	12
Squat	5	10–12
Leg Press	4	12
Hack Slide	4	12–15
Hamstring Curl	4	12–15
Bench Press	5	8–10
Incline Barbell Bench Press	4	10
Flat-Bench Dumbbell Flye	4	12
Deadlift	4	8
T-bar Row	4	12
Lat Machine Pulldown	4	12–15
Barbell Curl	5	10
Incline Dumbbell Curl	4	10–12
Close-grip EZ-bar Bench Press	5	8
Lying Triceps Extension	4	12
Seated Wrist Curl	4	12–15
Standing Calf Machine Heel Raise	4	12–15
Crunch	3	25

6

MENTAL OUTLOOK

Your Mind's Performance

Australia's Sonny Schmidt poses his amazing back.

Sandy Riddell starts the squat exercise.

Y ou don't have to have an IQ of 140 to apply your mind to athletic achievement. Right now I can think of a world-champion sprinter who has the IQ of a zucchini, and a top professional bodybuilder whose IQ isn't that much higher. But both individuals have developed a remarkable ability to isolate their ambitions, focus their minds, set goals, and follow through with positive action.

Peter C. Siegel is the leading authority on the subject of training the mind to excel in bodybuilding. He has coached many of the elite of the bodybuilding world. "Dealing with the mental aspect of mass training," he says, "has never been expanded upon. But you can exceed your expectations. When you really think about it, building muscle is an extension of a mental state, desire and belief being fused to stimulate goal-directed action."

Your mind must be applied to every aspect of your training. It is your thoughts that direct your efforts, methods, and applications of techniques. Without first thinking through your various steps to a perfect physique, you will be walking in a desert of despair with no roads to follow to any destination.

Regard your mind as a computer, a precise and able machine that you can program to do anything you desire.

Relax. Let your mind imagine inspiring thoughts of personal achievement. Ask yourself: What is it that I really want? Take your time. This is your dream of success, your body to build. "Seeing" in your mind's eye the type of physique you want to develop is the beginning of the process. You start with an idea. Log it in your mind (write it down if necessary), and follow through with a plan.

Are you one of those people in a rut? Do you do the same thing, more or less, every day? Are you a daily activity robot? Many people are bogged down with a boring life-style or have to work at jobs they dislike. Others are forced to work at two jobs just to pay their living expenses. Little time is left for anything else.

During my early twenties, I was a struggling artist living in the center of London. My

Lee Haney wins yet another Mr. Olympia title.

heroes were Henry Moore, Francis Bacon, and of course Pablo Picasso. To make a long story short, I failed to make a living as an artist. If I had known what I know now, maybe I would have succeeded. After moving to North America in the late sixties, I began to realize that getting ahead in life involved planning, not just ambition—and that planning had to be realistic, and it had to be executed.

Make a plan as to what you want in life. Write down a reasonable and workable agenda, and follow through with action. Simple? You bet it is. And it works.

Let's apply this plan of action to your bodybuilding goals. Do you want to have a proportionate, well-muscled body by next season? One that will turn heads and bring you admiring glances? Or are you into the contest scene? Do you want to win a local or even a state title? Or do your ambitions stretch to the Mr. or Ms. Olympia competition? Whatever your aspirations, they have to be founded in realism. It's no good trying to beat Lee Haney's or Cory Everson's champion-caliber physique if you're 40

years old and weigh 90 pounds. It's always unfortunate to have to admit that reaching the very pinnacle of a fantasy isn't always possible. Bodybuilding, like many other sports, is headed by those who are genetically gifted. These people still have to train vigorously and eat the right foods to get to the top, but the majority have some of the basic requirements to achieve their muscle-building goals. According to the researcher Herbert M. Sheldon, most top bodybuilders have mesomorphic, or naturally muscular, body types. Long-distance runners are invariably in the ectomorphic, or thin and lean, division. Sumo wrestlers, not surprisingly, are allocated the endomorphic classification of large-boned, massive body type.

Do you know what your potential is? You can seldom be 100 percent sure, but if you inherently possess long muscles that develop size and shape in response to exercise and have broad shoulders, narrow hips, and comparatively little body fat, then you could well be tailor-made for bodybuilding success. So make a plan according to your perceived potential.

France's Francis Benfatto

Long-Term Goals

Go on. Write them down. Set out on paper your dream of achievement. Be daringly realistic. This is your ultimate goal, remember, so don't be afraid to aim for the sky. After all, you don't have to let others in on your long-term ambitions for success. It can be your little secret for the time being.

Short-Term Goals

Now we really have to be brutally honest. Only set short-term goals that you can reach in four to six months. Adding five inches of pure muscle on your arms is too ambitious—go for one or two inches. Aim for a moderate increase in body weight. Target your bench press for no more than a 20 percent improvement. Remember that short-term goals must be reachable. After you have achieved them, it's time to reset more short-term targets. Chart a new course for success.

Bodybuilding mind expert Bob Wolff says, "Develop a new strategy that will take you off the beaten path and onto roads that are less travelled, and thus more exciting. Follow a new road map that will get you out onto the open roads, and explore those places where so few dare to go. If all you've done for your back are lat pulldowns, then it's time for some new scenery. How about trying T-bar rows, seated cable rows, or chins? The only limit to your progress will be your imagination."

Execution

Apply your mind to developing supercharged motivation. Your mindset at workout time will make or break you. Peter Siegel states, "You've got to reach out for more each workout. You must smash obstacles, striving, driving. You are the one who dictates the quality of mental fuel you're running on."

Regular isn't good enough; you have to run on super! This is where your mind focuses in like a computer. You must actively program yourself for success. Tell yourself that you are building your muscles bigger than ever. Imagine

"I'll show my arm anywhere," says Sandy Riddell.

your body growing as you exercise. Visualize success and growth with every rep. Condition your mind for an energized onslaught of developing pounds of muscle mass. Accept only positive vibrations. You have to channel your mind into every part of your free-weight routine, a program that has to be tailored to your individual needs. This book is designed to provide you with the knowledge to build the perfect bodybuilding routine and diet plan for your age, sex, ambition, tolerance to strenuous exercise, and recuperative powers.

Workout Meditation

When you put your mind to work along with your body, you will benefit by achieving total mental relaxation both before and after your workouts. A dose of stress-reducing meditation can be useful. Frank Zane, three-time Mr. Olympia, says, "A mind that is still receptive, and with enough concentrative meditation under your belt, can be evacuated relatively quickly and effi-

ciently. Modern psychologists stress that in order to really implant positive suggestion (great workouts), you must be relaxed."

You can actually slip into a few seconds of meditation before performing your last set of a specific exercise. Sit on the end of a bench in an erect posture with your back flat and head up. Place your hands on your knees. Face straight ahead but don't focus your eyes on any object. Direct your thought and sight inward. Take two deep breaths. Then say to yourself, "I am focused. This will be a supercharged set." After this affirmation, take one more deep breath, exhale completely, and assume your starting position for the exercise. Go for it!

As a bodybuilder with a purpose, you should never fail to understand that every change in your physiological state—your muscular development—is accomplished by an adjustment of focus in your mental outlook. And constant rehearsal of mind application will fine-tune your concentration to a point where you will benefit enormously.

7
PREVENTING INJURIES
Muscles, Tendons, and Joints

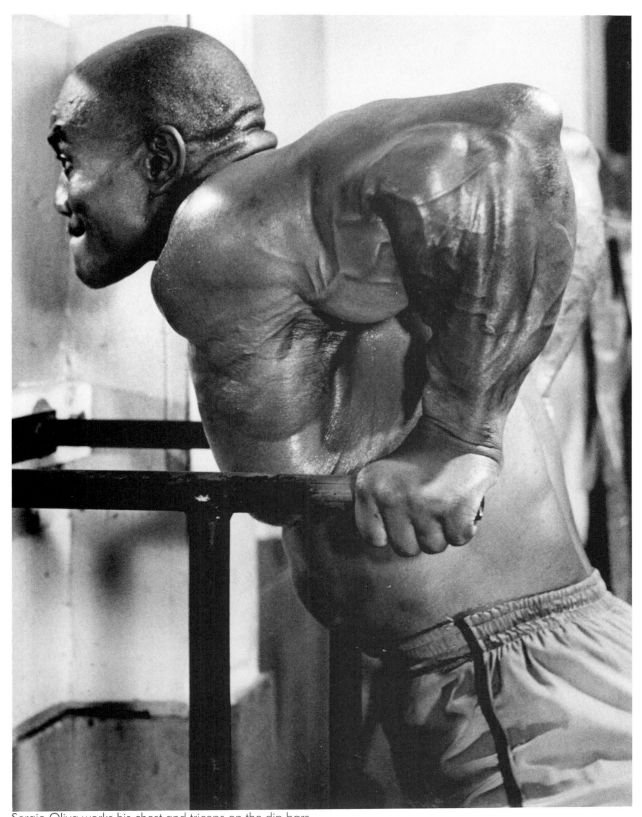

Sergio Oliva works his chest and triceps on the dip bars.

Joanne McCartney

Fortunately, bodybuilding is one of the safest sports. It doesn't involve the blows that occur in other contact recreational activities such as football, rugby, or hockey. Even soccer has its "barges," which can break your collarbone in no time flat. Methodical weight training within the normal range of motion of the joints avoids the ballistic moves of the golfer or baseball player, which almost invite injury to the shoulder joints from the wrenching, high-speed swings and throws needed to maximize performance.

But even so, with all its safety aspects and lack of aggressive contact, bodybuilders are still subject to injuries. Very few of the mishaps keep trainers out of the sport for good, but many have to hold back on training certain body areas or from using particular exercises because of a previous injury. Bob Lefavi, CSCS, a man of great knowledge on the subject of weight-training injuries, is adamant about one thing: "An ounce of prevention can save a pound of pain." He further advises that we "prepare and prevent rather than repair and repent."

In spite of this, one only has to visit a local hardcore gym (Gold's, World's, or Powerhouse) to see that young male and female bodybuilders are actively inviting injury in every corner of the gym. There's a difference between the sexes, though. Women generally are far more sensible than men about the way they safeguard themselves against needless injury. They train more methodically, use better exercise style, limit ballistic movements, and stretch and warm up more than their male counterparts. Men could learn a lot from watching women train. Ego still plays a big role in most men's workouts. One can almost see the rivers of testosterone coursing through their systems. At the drop of a hat, weights are slapped onto the bar, and training rhythms are turned into dangerous bouncing, arching, swinging, and leaning. It's little wonder that injuries occur. The body has numerous protective mechanisms that fall into place when we lift a particular weight, but still many people suffer injuries in spite of these mechanisms. Let's examine several of the factors that cause injuries and what you can do to prevent them.

Lisa Lorio performs Pek Dek flyes for her pecs.

Steroid Abuse

Dr. Barry Burton, a surgeon who has operated on scores of bodybuilders, states, "I have been struck by the fact that when I open up bodybuilders surgically, I see muscles that are huge but tendons that look relatively normal. Obviously, tendons adapt to progressive-resistance training and grow stronger, but tendons do not hypertrophy nearly as much as muscles. This leads to many tendon injuries."

Writing in the *Physical Culture Press*, Tom Deters confirms, "A research group at the University of Bristol in England examined the effects of steroids on tendons, concluding unequivocally that tendons were strengthened by resistance training but weakened by heavy steroid consumption."

Be aware that if you take steroids or any other drug that claims to increase muscle mass in an artificial and unnatural manner, you run the risk of wrecking your hormonal equilibrium and suffering the consequences of the adverse side effects of steroid abuse.

Dumbbell lateral raises done the Kathy Unger way.

Faulty Lifting Technique

The way you lift a weight is vitally important. Bob Lefavi insists, "It is not the velocity (how fast you move the bar) that predisposes us to injury, but the acceleration and deceleration of the bar (sudden starts and stops) that put us at risk. You can see how much acceleration of the bar can hurt us by understanding the following equation: Force = mass × acceleration + system weight. Here the 'force' is the weight you feel. 'Mass × acceleration' is the inertial force, and the 'system weight' is your weight plus that of the loaded bar (gravity force). This shows how important it is to maintain a controlled speed during a lift."

Keep your lifting techniques within the parameters of good form as much as possible. Perform movements that are slow, steady, and within the range of the joint's normal motion.

Weight Overload

The amount of weight you use is also important. Never suddenly increase the resistance by a large degree. Add poundage that is reasonable and within your ability to lift. Ego may play a significant part here. Many an injury has occurred when someone has tried to lift another person's weight that was far too heavy for him or her.

However, you must take care when exercising with moderate weights, too. High-rep sets can be dangerous if you perform them too quickly. The movement may become too fast and your reps could fall into the ballistic category. Lighter weight should be lifted slowly and with purpose, as if you are holding back a little.

Cold Temperatures

Your gym doesn't have to be a sweltering-hot environment for you to get a safe workout, but you should make sure that your muscles are warm. In cold temperatures, wear layers of clothing. As your body heats up, you can shed a layer at a time. Performing several sets of light (strict) reps may be necessary if your muscles are cold from inclement weather or freezing temperatures.

Overtraining

Overdoing your workouts can run down your physique rather than build it up. If you overtrain, the muscles become stringy and look flat. They do not pump well.

Bear in mind that if you train with very high intensity, you will need more rest between workouts. Heavy-duty training causes microtrauma, or small tears, in the muscle and connective tissue. The rate of repair in the connective tissue is slower because of the limited blood supply. Therefore, if heavy-duty training becomes too frequent, you may not be giving your muscles enough time for the ligaments and tendons to fully recover. There is a good case for alternating light and heavy workouts.

Gary Shankman, a licensed physical therapist at the Sports Medicine Foundation of America in Atlanta, Georgia, says, "Bodybuilders should pay far more attention to recuperation if they want to avoid injuries."

Nonexercise-Related Injuries

When I was attending art college in Norwich, England, I went to the movies with a buddy. During the film, my friend happened to sneeze. Whether it was the way he was sitting, or the unexpected suddenness of the sneeze, I'll never know, but the mishap caused a torn spleen and two broken ribs!

Most ruptures are caused by coughs or sneezes, rather than the practice of weight-training exercises. Moving furniture has caused many people to suffer injuries that lead to bad knees and elbow and back problems. Carelessness, jumping from heights, even dancing can cause injuries. I once asked a dozen paraplegics how they ended up in wheelchairs. Some of them, of course, were involved in car and bike accidents, but a surprising number of cases were caused by accidents such as falling out of bed or stepping off a curb and incurring a fall!

Steve Stallard

Troy Zuccolotto

Bent-over lateral raises done by Ming Chew.

"A good 95 percent of bodybuilding injuries I see could be prevented," says Douglas Smith. Make sure the time you spend when you're not exercising is accident-free, too.

Uneven Muscle Development

Keep your joints protected and reduce your risk of injury by training the antagonistic muscle groups around a joint. Many bodybuilders work their quads with excessive squats, hack slides, and thigh extensions, but neglect to work their hamstrings. Bob Paris, in his excellent book *Beyond Built!*, insists that hamstring movements should be no less than two-thirds that of the quad exercises. If you perform 12 sets for the quads, then balance must be preserved by working the hamstrings for at least eight sets.

In like manner, many bodybuilding beginners train their biceps muscles far more than their triceps, or their abdominals more than

their lower back. Balance of development is vital if you wish to remain injury-free.

Poor Nutrition

By comparing a car with your body, you can imagine in a very graphic way how misguided many of us are with regard to physical care. People will often clean and polish the outside of their car without ever considering whether the car's internal parts are being cared for, or fueled and oiled properly. Many of those same people will knowingly eat almost all their meals at fast-food restaurants, or take home TV dinners to heat in their microwave ovens.

What on earth is the point of caring for your body's outside surface without feeding it properly so that it stays healthy and runs well? Follow the guidelines in Chapter 12 for eating healthy, nourishing foods and following sound dietary habits. Good nutrition is not only a necessary agenda for top bodybuilding results, but it is vitally important in its role as an aid in preventing injury.

Changing Exercise Sequence

If you've spent years starting your workout with bench presses and then following with, for example, the heavy press-behind-neck exercise, then guard against suddenly changing the order around. When changes are made, the initial workouts should include less than all-out efforts. The body needs time to adjust to unfamiliar sequences of exercises. Start light and add weight systematically over the next few workouts. The same goes for new exercises or movements that you haven't done for years.

Recently, I did a few straight-arm pullovers. I can well remember using a 160-pound barbell for ten reps of this exercise. I loaded the bar to 50 pounds (a drop of 110 pounds!), but it was way too much! I ended up using the 20-pound bar only. It was only then that I realized I hadn't done a set of straight-arm pullovers for just over 30 years. No wonder 50 pounds felt heavy. I could have torn every muscle in my body! After three weeks of practice, I have now graduated to using 60 pounds. But that's enough—I'm content to use 100 pounds less

Samir Bannout poses for the camera.

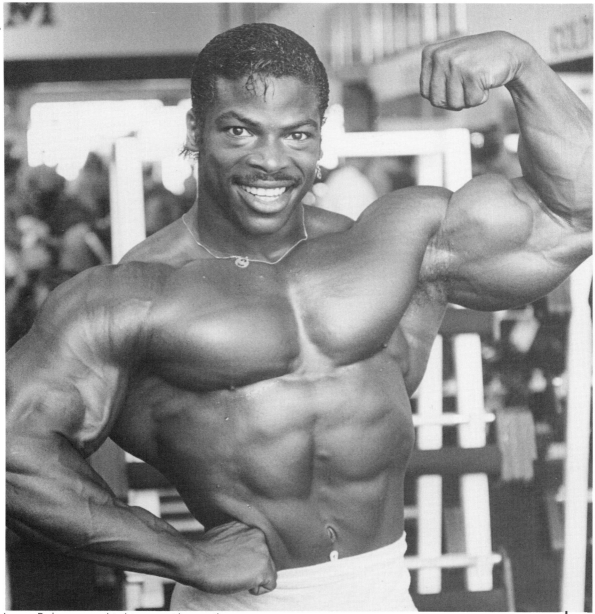

Aaron Baker poses his biceps with a smile.

than I did as an exuberant 20-year-old. And hopefully I'll remain injury-free in the process.

Just about everyone who performs progressive-resistance exercise has had to face injury that has set his or her training back for weeks or even months. It happens to the best of us. Art Zeller, Berry DeMey, Jeff Everson, Rick Valente, Johnny Fuller, Tom Platz, Al Beckles, Joe Bucci, Sergio Oliva, Chris Dickerson, Lou Ferrigno, Sly Stallone, and John Brown have all sustained severely torn muscles. Frank Zane, Cory Everson, and Arnold Schwarzenegger have

damaged their rotator-cuff joints. Even the strongest man in the world—Bill Kazmaier—knows the meaning of injury. And as for myself, through ignorance and stupidity while trying to increase my strength too quickly, I injured my right elbow, which needed surgery. Body-building is a great hobby. I don't regret working out for one minute, but the odds are against you training injury-free for the rest of your life. Take my advice. Do your best to "prepare and prevent rather than repair and repent."

8
MUSCULAR
DETAILS
Carving
Definition

Lee LaBrada exhibits proportion plus in a dramatic back pose.

Robert Rothrock is bulked to the max!

A few years back, I was lying on the sand somewhere between the dip bars and the chin-up bars on Santa Monica Beach. Even though I was literally cooking under the sun, my enjoyment was further increased as I drank a cup of hot tea. A copy of *Muscle and Fitness* magazine completed my feeling of contentment.

After thumbing through the magazine and downing my tea, I took to California's favorite beach pastime—people watching. As always, there was a tremendous mix of individuals and a surprisingly large number of people who obviously took regular exercise as part of their lifestyle. There were wrestlers, gymnasts, powerlifters, and bodybuilders.

Of course, I watched the bodybuilders. Here were guys training to look physically impressive, yet for the most part, they missed the mark. True enough, some looked striking, a few were magnificent, but many in their quest to add more and more mass were overweight, carrying too much body fat, and frequently showing uneven proportion. Far from looking well built and attractive, these guys moved awkwardly and almost appeared grotesque.

And then came the women—loads of them. Everyone was eyeing everyone else. The bodybuilders were confident because of their huge muscle mass. After all, didn't they have 50-inch chests going steady with 18-inch arms? But the two fellows who raised the female pulse rates most were a young surfer and a gymnast. Both had pleasantly wide shoulders and a narrow waist, both had abs, both had definition, both had muscular detail. And amazingly, both had arms that measured *under* 14 inches!

The Answer: Muscle Proportion

I pondered the question of how a guy with a 40-inch chest and 13½ inch arms could look physically superior to another with a 50-inch chest and 18-inch arms. The answer, of course, lies with proportion, definition, posture, and low body fat. A ripped physique will always win over

Sandy Riddell

Rick Riedel

a bulky physique. If you want both, then you have to build mass and quality muscle at the same time, while keeping your body-fat percentage low.

I am very much against performing abbreviated bodybuilding programs. I know that Peary Rader and many *Iron Man* magazine writers of the past liked to promote short exercise programs involving only squats, bench presses, and rows, but that technique never made sense to me. "A simple, basic routine," says trainer Vince Gironda, "will only build a simple, basic physique."

The idea that one should start bodybuilding by following a drastically abbreviated routine of standard exercises to build basic mass is a poor approach to building an impressive body. We were told to first build the foundation, and then, when we had some mass to play with, we could carve in the cuts and work the smaller muscles like the forearms, calves, and abs.

Agreed, multi-joint exercises are good mass builders, but even beginners should incorporate exercises that work the entire body. Contrary to what the abbreviated-routine advocates advise, the small muscles will *not* take care of themselves if you only train the big ones. We need to start bodybuilding as we mean to go on; that is to say, we should include exercises for the calves, abs, lower back, intercostals, brachialis, traps, forearms, upper pecs, rhomboids, tibialis, biceps, rear delts, and hamstrings.

It's the attention to muscle detail that gives you the finishing touches. Detail gives you the judges' nod. Detail brings respect and admiration from the crowd. Detail raises the room temperature when you make your entry on the stage of competition.

Your first thoughts should involve the degree of adipose cells you are carrying. A layer of fat over your physique actually makes your muscles look soft. But there's more. Fat takes away your shape. And something that has no shape has no visual appeal.

Beginners don't have to perform specialized exercise movements for the tibialis, rhomboids, or the brachialis, but all-encompassing

Dumbbell rows done the Troy Zuccolotto way. He's an advocate of shape training.

movements should be used so that these fringe muscle sections are at least brought into play during your workouts.

The Objective Assessment

Each of us has body parts that grow easily while other areas are slow to respond. This is where self-assessment has to come in. You must learn to look at your body with an objective eye. Admittedly, some bodybuilders find that their necks or forearms, for example, grow along with the rest of their muscles. They don't need specialized exercises for these areas. Other trainers have to really blitz stubborn body parts to get them to grow.

Whether you are training to compete in a bodybuilding contest, or just want to look good on the beach, you have to shape your muscles with proportion in mind. Don't let your quads get so bulked up that your calves disappear. If there's a tendency for underdeveloped forearms, then work them twice a week. If your serratus muscles don't stand out in bold relief, work in some pullovers during every chest workout. No back flair to the lats? Never miss out on wide-grip chins. Lacking low abdominals? Make the hanging knee raise a regular exercise in every waist workout. Weak lower back? Try hyperextensions. If you have rounded shoulders that lack rear deltoid development, bent-over flyes are the answer. Need harder, more rounded glutes? Try the low cable straight-leg kick-back. Keep that body looking good by building muscle detail.

The Definition Routine

Today more than ever, bodybuilders are keeping that defined look by allotting one or two workouts a week to shape training. Physical culturist Troy Zuccolotto says, "I combine two forms of training. One day I train heavy (aiming to lift maximum weights). The next time I hit that same body part, I follow a 'feel' workout. The heavy day builds mass, which is the primary purpose of training. The next 'feel' workout develops definition, separation, and detail. I really believe this form of training so refined my physique that I won the National U.S.A. Championship."

Don't make the definition routine a light workout; it can be quite the contrary. Use a little less weight, but concentrate on working the muscle more completely. As Arnold Schwarzenegger says, "I used to use a lot of weight. Not anymore. I now find that concentration lends its own form of resistance. By thinking, I can direct the effort."

Before a heavy-weight workout, program yourself to think about getting that weight off your chest in the bench press, or heaving up that T-bar in the rowing exercise. When the definition workout is underway, make up your mind to use good form and strict execution. Deepen your muscularity and etch in that detail with full-range movements that will pump blood into the muscle and give you a quality physique.

Take It from Vince

The king of muscle detail is veteran trainer Vince Gironda. Way back in the forties, he was building muscles on people where many didn't even know they had muscles. For example, Vince wasn't in favor of using heavy squats exclusively for building the quads. "The thigh is divided up into several areas," says the Iron Guru. "We need thigh sweep, lower vastus internus, thigh biceps, sartorius and thigh rods. The squat exercise won't give you half of these aspects."

One impressive muscle detail can be created by developing the trapezius muscle in back of the neck. It gives you that hulking look when you are in the relaxed position. All the most popular Mr. Olympias had enormous traps.

Of course, using a wide variety of exercises will help etch in muscular detail, but that's somewhat of an overgeneralized approach. The ideal attack is to assess your physique first, decide on a plan of action, tailor a workout program to precisely fit your physical needs . . . and go to work. After three months of training, your appearance will improve tremendously.

Rich Gaspari congratulates Lee Haney on his Mr. Olympia crown.

9

DEVELOPING YOUR BODY

Part by Part

Head-to-toe muscles displayed by Tonya Knight.

Backs galore! Francis Benfatto, Mike Christian, and Rich Gaspari go for it.

At first glance, bodybuilding may appear to be no more than the random lifting of weights in an assortment of positions—bench presses, squats, curls, rows, etc. But there's more to it than that. There's a much more scientific approach.

Even though some skeptics believe that our bodies cannot be shaped according to a plan, after nearly 35 years in the sport, I take the view that muscle areas *can* be defined. More than that—I categorically *know* that a body can be changed. But the first requirement is a little patience, because individual muscles cannot be *dramatically* shaped overnight. The process works, but it takes a little time and a rational mind.

To me, the term "bodybuilding" isn't such an accurate one, but unfortunately it has stuck. I would far prefer to describe it as body sculpting or physical culture, but the term is here to stay. I hate it because it neglects the subtleties of the sport. It's not just *bodybuilding*—it's shaping the body, designing it to be more balanced and attractive. This is exactly what so-called hardcore bodybuilders dislike. They are only interested in ripped muscle mass. Aesthetics don't come into it. Shape and proportion are dirty words. Hardcore bodybuilders today like to call people like Steve Reeves and Frank Zane "pencil-necks"!

They are criticized for not being massive enough, despite the fact that their shape and proportion are amazingly impressive!

Our view of the human body is directed by our degree of maturity and sophistication. For example, when we are children, we are impressed by the size of big, rotund people. Later, in our teens, we may turn our admiration toward huge professional wrestlers. It doesn't matter that they don't have a cut of muscle definition in their bodies, or that they are overweight.

Next in order, to win our praise, may be the hardcore bodybuilder. The big pecs, heavy quads, and thick back impress us. Never mind that the subject may have turnip thighs, small calves, and no abs, or that he can't throw a baseball, couldn't jump over a tennis net, and abhors the thought of walking more than 100 yards for fear of losing some muscle mass.

Today the sport of bodybuilding is not in the hands of those whose appreciation extends far beyond the basic ripped mass of the hardcore bodybuilder. The most proportionate, symmetrical, and balanced builds seldom take home the top prize in physique contests. Bodybuilding will never have complete acceptance among the nations of the world while judges award top titles to misshapen physiques.

Why do judges vote for muscle size above everything else? Well, for one thing, it's the most measurable and safe criterion for choosing a winner. To a judge, the "best" chest or "best" legs are invariably the biggest. The concept is unbelievable to me, but so true. Since when is a work of art assessed purely for its size?

Physical beauty, proportion, balance, and shape, in addition to adequate mass, should be rewarded above anything else. Mr. and Ms. Olympia awards, therefore, should go to athletes like Bob Paris, Lee LaBrada, Juliette Bergman, Tonya Knight, Anja Langer, Cory Everson, and the most perfect physique on earth at this current writing—Francis Benfatto!

Now let's examine each body part, for which I will give you the best exercises for muscle development, along with valuable training tips.

You can't help but admire the virtually perfect physique of France's Francis Benfatto.

Germany's svelte Anja Langer

Arms

This is an area of the body that holds a fascination for almost everyone. An impressive arm is one that has a proportionate balance between the biceps, bracchial, and triceps muscles. This upper arm has to have *balance* with the forearms. Thin people are often able to build up splendid upper arms but fall short when it comes to their forearm development. Most bodybuilders, however, find that specialized forearm training is unnecessary because almost every exercise works the area to some extent. An indication of the truth of my point is Canadian bodybuilder Steve Brisbois, who has the most amazing forearms imaginable, yet who *never* trains them with specialized forearm exercises.

Biceps

Best Exercises

Standing Barbell Curl
Incline Dumbbell Curl (45 degrees)
Seated Alternate Dumbbell Curl
Preacher Bench Curl
Seated Concentration Curl

Tips

- Never perform low reps with heavy weight for biceps work. The tendon structure around the elbow is too delicate and you may sustain an injury.
- Biceps exercises should be varied frequently. Change one exercise in your biceps routine every three weeks.
- The lower biceps (near the elbow) are trained with 30- to 40-degree preacher bench curls.
- The biceps peak is developed most effectively by doing the concentration curl with light weights, using as much mind power to concentrate effort into the peaking process as possible. Squeeze the biceps hard at the top of each movement.

Concentration curls performed by Ron Love.

Triceps

Best Exercises

Close-grip Parallel Bar Dip
Lying Triceps Stretch
Close-grip EZ-bar Bench Press
Lat Machine Pressdown
Shoulder-width-grip reverse Bench Press
Standing Barbell Triceps Stretch
Cradle Bench Cable-Triceps Extension
Single-dumbbell Triceps Extension (across chest)

Tips

- Don't neglect to perform multi-joint triceps movements, such as close-grip bench presses and parallel bar dips, which build that triceps thickness.
- Resist the temptation to use very heavy weights in single-joint exercises, such as single-dumbbell triceps stretches, triceps pressdowns, etc. You will end up with permanent elbow problems.
- Never neglect work on the outer triceps head. Its full development gives the arm an appeal that cannot be duplicated by mass alone.
- The best "outer head" triceps exercises are the cradle bench cable triceps extension and the across-chest single dumbbell triceps extension.

Forearms

Best Exercises

Barbell Wrist Curl
Hammer Curl
Reverse Barbell Wrist Curl
Zotman Curl

Tips

- The forearms are developed and worked in a secondary manner during virtually all arm exercises using free weights.
- Exercises like chin-ups, lat pulldowns, curls, and deadlifts work the forearms more significantly than shoulder, chest, and triceps exercises.
- Although only a small percentage of top bodybuilders train their forearms regularly with specific exercises, it is accepted that increased forearm development will occur if you perform a forearm routine two or three times weekly.
- The most effective forearm movement is the barbell wrist curl (palms up).

Everyone sees Samir Bannout do parallel bar dips.

Look at the muscle-carved legs of Gary Strydom.

Eddie Robinson

Legs

Although all bodybuilders have to train their legs hard, especially if they want to compete successfully in bodybuilding contests, it is nevertheless true that some people have what can only be termed "natural legs." People like Steve Reeves, Bill Pearl, Bob Paris, Frank Zane, Tom Platz, Mohammed Benazizza, Berry DeMey, Eddie Robinson, David Dearth, Juliette Bergman, Cory Everson, Anja Langer, Shelley Beatie, and Tonya Knight all have naturally impressive leg development. Others such as Arnold Schwarzenegger, Mike Christian, Serge Nubret, Dave Draper, Tony Pearson, and even Lee Haney have had to practically sweat blood to maximize their leg development.

Quadriceps

Best Exercises

Back Squat
Leg Press (45 degrees)
Front Squat
Hacklift
Thigh Extension
Lunge
Sissy Squat

Tips

- Squats are indisputably the king of all leg exercises. Beginners should gradually work up to performing three sets of squats every leg workout. Ultimately, five or six sets should be your goal.
- Do not habitually perform very heavy, low-rep squats. Never bounce in the lowest bent-knee position; otherwise, knee, hip-joint, and lower-back injuries could become a reality.
- Keep constant vigilance over your lower thigh development. Front squats, hack slides, or sissy squats should be included in your routine so that the lower thighs are worked adequately.
- The quads often respond well to high-rep attacks. Don't be afraid to experiment with reps soaring into the thirties and forties.

Hamstrings

Best Exercises

Lying Leg Curl
Standing Single-leg Curl
Straight-leg Deadlift

Tips

- Try half-leg curls, holding a dumbbell between your feet for your often neglected lower hamstrings.
- Experiment not only with moderate slow reps (10 to 15 per set), but also with sets of very quick, pumping high reps (50 to 60 per set).

Calves

Best Exercises

Standing Calf Raise (machine)
Donkey Calf Raise
Seated Calf Raise
Toe Press (45°-degree leg machine)

Tips

- Always stretch the calves for ten minutes before training them with weights or machines. Stand on a block or a stair and raise up and down slowly, stretching your heels to the ground as much as possible. Use a leg press machine with no weight for a similar stretching effect.
- Learn to use your calves to thrust your body into motion when walking, running, or climbing stairs.
- Calves that resist development may benefit from three or four training sessions weekly instead of two.

Mishay Santos works the thigh extension machine.

Shoulders

The shoulders are three-headed muscles, and all three sections need to be specifically trained. The side deltoids need attention to give the torso that wide-shoulder look. Rear deltoid development is required to counteract any round-shouldered appearance. The front deltoids are essential for an impressive lat spread and the "most muscular" and double biceps poses from the rear. The front delts form the upper shoulder height in the double biceps pose.

Aaron Baker reps out with lateral raises.

Best Exercises
Press Behind Neck
Dumbbell Lateral Raise
Bent-over Lateral Raise
Upright Row
Military Press
Seated Dumbbell Press
Alternate Forward Dumbbell Raise

Tips
- Because of their complex structure, the deltoids are injured easily. Warm up completely before using heavy weights. When high resistance is used, make a strong effort to use strict control.
- Base your deltoid training around the press-behind-neck exercise, which by far is the most effective shoulder-bulking movement.
- Work all three deltoid heads during every shoulder workout.
- For shoulders that resist development, try the pre-exhaust system. Alternate three to four sets each of upright rows and dumbbell presses. Rest no longer than it takes to change weights.

Alternate dumbbell forward raises executed by California's Brad Verrett.

An amazing back display by Barbados-born Albert Beckles.

Back

As far as bodybuilding is concerned, the back consists of three distinct muscle areas: latissimus dorsi (lats), lumbar region (lower back), and trapezius (traps). Each section has its own group of exercises.

One point about back training has emerged. Virtually no bodybuilder has developed an outstanding back without the performance of wide-grip chin-ups. In fact, those who either can't or won't do chin-ups invariably have what is known as a weak back appearance.

Francis Benfatto performs a dramatic back pose.

Traps

Situated at the base of the back of the neck, the traps can be seen from both the front and the back. They form that attractive, herculean slope seen to advantage in top bodybuilders like Arnold Schwarzenegger, Lee Haney, Serge Nubret, and Gary Strydom.

Best Exercises

Dumbbell Shrug
Barbell Shrug
Barbell Clean
Deadlift
Upright Row

Tips

• If you possess a very short neck, then you may be giving your traps sufficient exercise during your regular workouts. You may not need specialized trap exercises. Medium- or long-necked bodybuilders should work their traps regularly.

• Take a tip from Lee Haney. Use the behind-back barbell shrug and bend your arms at the highest point of the lift, endeavoring to lift the barbell as high as possible.

• The traps respond well to both high (20 to 30) repetitions and low (5 to 7) repetitions. Use both in your workouts.

• Practice the "most muscular" pose daily; nothing builds and isolates the traps better than this pose.

Lower Back

Known as the seat of power, lower back development is often the deciding factor when judges try to determine a winner between two otherwise evenly balanced physiques.

Best Exercises

Prone Hyperextension
Straight-leg Deadlift
Bent-knee Deadlift
Barbell Clean

Tips

- By far the safest lower back movement is the prone hyperextension. Try sets of 12 to 15 reps of this exercise.
- Beware of using any type of ballistic movement when performing straight-leg deadlifts of any kind. Keep your back flat when performing barbell rowing motions and bent-knee deadlifts. Injury in the lower back is common if you strain it using too much weight.

Lats

The lats have two aspects of development: thickness and flair. Thickness is built from rowing exercises, and flair results from wide-grip chin-ups on a horizontal bar, and wide-grip pulldowns on a lat machine.

Bodybuilding exercises alone will not teach you to show your lat development to full advantage. The lats have to be posed out repeatedly before they have real visual impact.

Best Exercises

T-bar Row
Wide-grip Chin-up Behind Neck
Seated Cable Row
Wide-grip Lat Pulldown
Close-grip Lat Pulldown
Single-arm Dumbbell Row

Tips

- Perform wide-grip chin-ups during every lat workout. You can chin to the front or the back of the neck, but in either case, keep your elbows spread rearward. Chinning with your elbows forward puts too much emphasis on the arm muscles.
- Practice a few lat spreads every night in front of your bathroom mirror before going to bed. This will maximize scapula flexibility and keep your lats loose and ready whenever you want to show them off.
- Finish every lat workout with one set of wide-grip pulldowns; do a full 30 reps.

Lisa Lorio starts the close-grip lat pulldown.

Lisa Lorio begins the wide-grip chin-up.

She pulls up to the finish of the exercise.

Mohammed Benazizza

Krista Anderson crunches her abdominals.

Abdominals

Everybody wants well-defined abdominal ridges; hardcore bodybuilders want veritable "bricks" of ab muscles.

Bear in mind that performing endless sit-ups and leg raises won't give you super abs. The exercises may help build up some muscle (even though they are not the best midsection exercises), but if there is a layer of fat covering them, the abdominals will fail to show clearly. The first secret of attaining abdominal impressiveness is to obtain an overall low body-fat percentage.

* * *

That's it, folks! All the exercises that you need to develop your body have been covered. Now you're ready to hit the gym. Go to it! You have my best wishes and encouragement. I wish you every success and happiness with your bodybuilding goals.

Best Exercises
  Crunch
  Hanging Leg Raise
  Seated Knee-in
  Broomstick Twist
  Roman Chair Curl-up Twist

Tips
- Once you have reduced your body fat, your upper abs build easily. Throw your concentrated effort into working the lower abs during each workout. The upper abs will take care of themselves.
- Don't use heavy weights for your abdominal exercises because the midsection is composed of many intricate muscle fibres. Muscle tears or even a rupture could result.
- Perform ab workouts regularly but not excessively. Long, drawn-out waist workouts could stop you from gaining mass. Ab workouts shouldn't exceed 15 minutes.
- Practice the abdominal vacuum to tone your entire ab region. Breathe in, and then exhale quickly. Suck in your stomach without taking in air and hold for five seconds. Relax. Breathe deeply and repeat the process several times a day.

Samir Bannout is flanked by Krista and Dinah Anderson for a *Flex* magazine cover.

10

CREATIVE CHEATING

Do It
with Care

Jackie Paisley and Sandy Riddell on stage at the Ms. Olympia.

Matt DuFresne

You're young now, so you probably don't remember the old days when Bob Hoffman had his ongoing feud with Joe Weider. Those were the days! It's all like a silly dream now, but it happened. The two biggest muscle-magazine publishers of the day would squabble over everything. They didn't argue face to face, nor even over the phone. No, sir. They carried on their feud in their magazines. And frequently things got ugly.

One of their eternal differences surrounded the question of exercise form. The Weider camp heartily endorsed the cheating principle. Joe Weider would extol the virtues of adding more and more weight resistance, using lots of swinging motion to hoist the weight up. "Cheating," said Joe Weider, "is the next logical step. If you want bigger and bigger muscles, you should use loose form in some exercises."

This kind of talk riled up Bob Hoffman. Through his publication, *Strength and Health*, he would fight off the "Trainer of Champions" with articles promoting the exclusive use of "perfect" (strict) exercise form. "Cheating is no good," he said. "Perfect exercise form is what builds a perfect physique."

Somehow Bob Hoffman had wrangled his way into being the "official" coach of the U.S. national weightlifting team, and he was hot on the three Olympia lifts: the press, the snatch, and the clean and jerk. So keen was Hoffman on the Olympic lifts that he seldom wrote a training article where he didn't recommend the use of these weightlifting moves. "Olympic lifts," wrote Hoffman, "are your key to physical greatness. You cannot build a strong-looking, massive Mr. Universe-type physique without them."

What Hoffman failed to realize at the time was the contradiction of denouncing cheating methods while extolling the bodybuilding virtues of movements such as the snatch and the clean and jerk. Both lifts, needless to say, involve an enormous degree of cheating. In fact, they could be described as the ultimate in cheating moves when it comes to hoisting barbells above the head. Is cheating good or bad for the bodybuilder? There are two points we know for sure. You *can* build muscle by performing *every* exer-

Lisa Lorio can stop a truck.

Sonny Schmidt

cise in loose (cheating) style. And you *can* build muscle by performing *every* exercise in strict style.

Bob Paris writes in *Beyond Built*, "Beginners should perform all their exercises in superstrict fashion. They are apprentices and need to learn the feel of performing a full range of motion, without body swing or bounce to springboard the weight aloft." There is a great deal of sense to this statement. Learn the basics and earn the right to improvise at a later (more advanced) stage. This same philosophy surely can be applied to music, painting, sculpture, sports, chess, and any number of endeavors. We can only master a technique by first learning it in a studied apprenticeship.

In a sense, the word "cheating," when applied to bodybuilding, is a misnomer. Your aim is to build muscle, and there is no such thing as a cheating exercise to develop mass. It's a different matter when it comes to lifting a weight in competition. Obviously, if a powerlifter disobeys the rules by lifting his buttocks off the bench during a bench press, then that athlete *is* cheating. The term applies, and the lift is invalid.

But the cheating principle is very real in bodybuilding. When used properly, it can prove effective in building bigger muscles. I cannot, however, generalize about cheating by saying that all curls should be performed with a swinging motion. I cannot advise people to bounce when in the low squat position of the deep kneebend. Each exercise has its own limitations. Some exercises should *never* be executed in loose style. Other movements work best if they are *always* performed in loose style, while still more exercises lend themselves to both strict and loose performance. Let me apply this thinking to some common exercises.

Squat

I can well remember reading articles that recommended "jumping squats" while holding a barbell across the shoulders. It's difficult to imagine a more dangerous exercise. Not only would the hip and thigh bone sockets take a pounding, almost guaranteeing a hip-

Dinah Anderson completes an incline bench press.

replacement operation in later life, but the knees would take a punishment of unbelievable stress. Ladies and gentlemen of iron . . . leave jumping squats out of your routine.

Actually, all squats, heavy and light, should be performed in a strict fashion. You should descend fairly slowly (only until your legs are parallel to the floor if you suspect weakness in the knee area), and rise upwards by thrusting with the thighs. Keep your head upright and your body as vertical as possible.

"Never bounce out of the low squat position," says Shawn Ray. "It is the most suicidal thing you can do for your knees." You may get away with it for several years, but believe me, one day you'll regret it!

Bench Press

Here is another no-cheating exercise. Don't raise your hips off the bench. Don't drop the weight quickly so that it bounces on your chest. Many a cracked sternum has resulted from this. Admittedly, bouncing the bar into orbit and thrusting with the hips will give you another 30 pounds of overall poundage, but there will not be a corresponding increase in pectoral growth.

Kathy Unger shows super form in a single-arm dumbbell curl.

Curl

Now comes your chance for creative cheating. The curl is one of those exercises that can benefit from a variety of exercise styles. You can lean back against an upright support and perform your curls in a superstrict fashion, or you can merely stand upright with your elbows locked above your hip bones, and curl the weight up and down with no upper arm movement at all. (This no-cheating method is sometimes called the "body drag" curl because the bar almost drags along the torso as it is raised and lowered.)

Now consider cheating curls. "The normal and most accepted method is to perform the first six to eight reps in good style, and then when further strict reps are impossible, you allow for progressively looser style for the final few repetitions," says seven-time Mr. Olympia Arnold Schwarzenegger.

The other alternative is to use considerably increased weight so that the *entire* set is performed in a loose exercise style. Warning: If you choose the latter method, make sure that your biceps have been adequately warmed up with at least two sets of reps with a moderately heavy weight.

Lateral Raise

Now here's an exercise where we can really get creative. But don't get carried away with using very heavy weights. The deltoid muscles are very intricate, and injury is common. When using the cheating principle in the lateral raise exercise, your only concern should be to pulverize the deltoid muscles. Keep the elbows slightly bent so that unwanted stress is kept away from the elbow joints. Start by bending forward and then, with just the right amount of swing, raise the dumbbells upward. It's important to proceed with the cheating principle in a properly executed style, never just swinging the weight up. After all, the cheating method is designed to get us past a sticking point so that we can *feel* the resistance working the easier parts of the exercise range.

Ming Chew is caught in the middle of a dumbbell lateral raise.

Heavy barbell rows are part of Ken "Flex" Wheeler's back training.

Rowing

A little heave-ho can be used on the T-bar row machine, but it's a good idea to "counter" your cheat moves by also performing some strict exercises. Do a few strict sets of T-bar rows (with the arms straightened all the way down to stretch the lats) to round out your routine.

One of the most common mistakes bodybuilders make is to try to perform Mentzer-bar (palms-in) pulldowns in a superstrict manner. The same is true for the seated cable row. There's no way these two exercises should be performed strictly without back movement. Both exercises should be performed in the same manner as one would row a boat. There *has* to be a forward stretch and subsequent rearward lean to fully involve the lat muscles.

Sonny Schmidt shows a fantastic lat spread.

Standing Press

Whenever I think about cheating in the standing press, I think of that scene in the movie *Pumping Iron* where Lou Ferrigno is shoving up an Olympic bar while his dad is counting reps and encouraging him to keep going.

Your delts can benefit from performing cheat presses (jerks), semi-cheat presses (push-presses), and strict presses (military). Be careful, however, not to fall into the trap of leaning back while push-pressing. Too much resistance will be placed on the front delts, and little will be felt on those all-important side deltoids.

Always use common sense when employing the cheat principle. It can be dangerous because you are asking your body to do the impossible. You cheat when you can't lift a weight in normal strict form. Err on the side of

safety by not trying to lift or press more than you can handle.

Since your ability to lower weights is greater than your ability to raise them, bodybuilders can benefit from cheating a weight upward and then lowering it slowly. Some even claim that this negative part of an exercise is the most important part. Certainly it can be beneficial, but don't do what one bodybuilder did some years ago. He took a 120-pound dumbbell, propped his elbow into his groin, and jerked the weight up with a heave-ho type of curling action. He then proceeded to lean backward and slowly lower the weight in a negative curl. Snap! Crackle! Pop! That was it. His biceps tore out of its insertion at the elbow, and he needed surgery to repair it.

11

AVOIDING BURNOUT

Harness Your Energy

New York's Ming Chew performs triceps stretches.

One of the world's best "most muscular" poses shown by Shawn Ray.

Mohammed Benazizza and Dorian Yates both get the arms-up vote from *Muscle and Fitness* publisher Joe Weider.

Armand Tanny said: "Burnout is a phenomenon of the modern world. After high-level output, some people's energy, enthusiasm, and even visions of accomplishment deteriorate into boredom, cynicism, and despair."

Energy is vitality. It's your individual capacity for action, the natural force you exert when you train, run, work, or make love. Bodybuilding, by its very nature, requires tremendous amounts of energy. Having energy for life is exhilarating. Not having it is devastating. Energy gets you up in the morning, propels you to the gym, and powers you through your workout.

Some people always appear to have enormous energy levels; others seem perpetually drained. In truth, your energy levels are often genetically determined. However, if you find yourself low in energy or in a state of apparent burnout, then disaster could be lurking. We can't touch energy because of its intangibility, but we

can take steps to generate more of it! The inability of a muscle to pump may be your sign of having burnout. Other symptoms are fatigue, flagging interest, irritability, loss of appetite, depression, lack of motivation, and excessive muscle soreness. As the bodybuilder digs deeper into an overtrained condition, the evidence becomes more explicit: insomnia, onset of allergies, increased susceptibility to colds and other infections, and a higher percentage of training injuries.

If you get into this state, the only reasonable answer is to exercise less often or take a break from training altogether. Beginning bodybuilders should be able to avoid burnout by never training two days in a row.

Is there a scientific way of determining whether you are overtraining? Since being able to interpret your body's warning signals can be difficult unless you have a huge amount of training experience, I suggest you test yourself by

Van Smith

taking your pulse early in the morning. Pulse checks are actually scientific. Lie quietly in bed after you wake up in the morning and take your pulse. Then get out of bed and weigh yourself. Write down both your weight and pulse count. Later in the day, after training, lie down for 15

minutes without sleeping. Now check your pulse again. Get up and weigh yourself. Record both your pulse and weight again. If your pulse rate after a workout is higher than it was that morning before your workout, you have not fully recovered from the workout. You should either rest more or not train at all. If you are losing weight, this is another indication of overtraining. The early morning pulse rate and the post-training rate should be approximately the same as you near your peak. When you go beyond your peak, you invite burnout to set in. The very muscles you strive to build will shrink, and your fire of enthusiasm will desert you as well.

What can you do to build your energy level, avoid burnout, and put yourself into an ideal position to give everything to your workouts? Read my advice on the topics that follow.

Avoid Junk Foods

Junk foods clog up your system. Avoid sugar- and salt-loaded items. The worst foods include: candies, chocolates, sugary crullers, doughnuts, potato chips, cream, sour cream, bacon, cream cheese, highly processed meats, and deep-fried foods of all kinds.

Junk foods supply little but empty calories, and they do more harm than good. Not only do they contribute to the growth of body fat, but they can hasten the onset of diseases associated with obesity. More to the point of this chapter, junk foods rob you of your natural energy. You may get a short-lived rush of energy from some high-sugar foods, but the ultimate effect is a plummeting energy level just when you are looking for a sustained level of endurance for your training.

Simple sugars have a high glycemic index rating because they are converted into glucose very rapidly. Glucose has a glycemic index value of 100 and is the basis on which all other foods are judged. Now you might expect a simple sugar such as fructose to have a high energy rating on the glycemic scale, but it's only 20. On the other hand, a potato has a glycemic index of 90, which makes it a poor pre-workout food. Fructose is better. You need foods with a low

France's Marie Mahabir

glycemic index to deliver a sustained amount of energy, not the quick rush delivered by glucose, which makes your blood sugar soar and then drop quickly. You need a sustained flow to get you through your workout-healing process, in which catabolic waste materials are removed in preparation for the anabolic musclebuilding process that follows.

Eat five or six times a day whether you are trying to gain or lose weight but eat less on rest days. If you overeat on rest days, you could add unwanted fat, which will prove hard to shed.

The best carbohydrate foods according to the glycemic index are: fructose (20), whole-wheat spaghetti (42), oatmeal (49), yams (51), skim milk (32), soy beans (15), lentils (29), peanuts (13), apples (39), grapefruit (26), and cherries (23). The worst carbohydrate foods are: maltose (105), glucose (100), cornflakes (80), carrots (92), potatoes (90), and honey (87).

Troy Zuccolotto rips through a set of cable curls.

Stay Motivated

Energy levels are oftentimes associated with our enthusiasm. Try to keep positive thoughts in your mind. Don't become pessimistic or a grumbler. Negative thinking will drain you of physical well-being. Read bodybuilding magazines, attend bodybuilding shows, and view training videos regularly. Keep your enthusiasm for success high. Enthusiasm goes hand in hand with high-energy levels.

Tobacco

Smoking is one of the most harmful habits for human beings. On an average, every cigarette you smoke reduces your life expectancy by eleven minutes. Not only does smoking diminish your aerobic condition dramatically, but it also increases the likelihood that you'll develop heart disease, cancer of the lungs and stomach, emphysema, and circulatory diseases. To top it off, smokers often develop a hacking cough, lung congestion, and frequent headaches.

Smoking does not go with bodybuilding. I have known many bodybuilders who smoked. At first, they didn't seem to be harmed by the habit, but gradually their workouts became harder and harder to complete. High-rep squats were the first to go. Gradually the cigarettes drained each bodybuilder of his or her vitality. Their workouts got fewer and fewer, until they were dropped entirely.

Fresh Air and Sunshine

Do you live your whole life indoors or in your car? If you do, chances are you spend most of your time breathing stale air. What's worse, you could be inhaling smoke or fumes if your workplace isn't properly ventilated. Over the years, I have known several bodybuilders who worked in poorly ventilated environments—garages, chemical plants, asbestos factories, and foundries. When I heard their complaints, I would always advise them to quit, but few did. Now some have even passed away prematurely.

The wide-grip chin-up done by Samir Bannout.

You need fresh air and sunshine. However, avoid prolonged exposure to the sun, especially if you are prone to get a burn. Regular fresh air and sunshine will help increase your vitality level.

Mohammed Benazizza (left) and Dorian Yates pose down at the Night of the Champions.

Overtraining

Working out too hard and too long can lead to burnout. If you don't recover or mend before your next workout, you will drive yourself into a deep sticking point. You will be overtrained.

Make a point of building up the intensity and length of your workouts on a gradual basis. Be content to start slowly. Train with only one light set if need be. Build up the poundage and number of sets systematically, being careful to stay within the parameters of complete recovery. Too many trainers succumb to the enthusiasm of the moment and unknowingly train themselves into a rut. Many is the time that I have felt so energetic and strong during my workouts that I have been too enthusiastic with intensity levels, too hyped by the euphoria, and too spellbound by the movements. This would cause me to overtrain, only to find a nagging headache greeting me the next day. This is very common among older trainers.

Alcohol and Drugs

I have known champion bodybuilders who have trained while drinking vodka, and others who could only work out after smoking a joint. I don't know how they managed it. If I have a couple of beers, I'm good for nothing. Fatigue sets in and I feel like lying down and taking a nap rather than going to the gym.

Drinking alcohol or taking drugs can be your downfall, especially if it becomes habit-forming. Excessive consumption, of course, will ruin you totally. Take a look at any hardened substance abuser and you'll see what I mean.

Steroids

Steroid abuse definitely robs you of energy. At first, workouts go better than ever. You feel stronger and recover more quickly from hard-training sessions. And you may even notice you have an increase in energy. But in time, there is a complete change for the worse. Muscles that once bounced with vitality and tone soon become soft and bloated. Joints, previously flexible and strong, turn stiff and ache constantly. Energy levels formerly at a glorious height plummet to a depressingly low plateau.

I remember once meeting a top physique star at the World Gym in California. He could hardly drag himself across the gym floor. He was loaded with steroids and had been taking them on and off for the better part of ten years. He admitted to me that he had no energy and his muscles and joints ached from head to toe. His sex life was nonexistent, and his wife was leaving him. He also had been suffering from pain in his kidneys for months. I told him he needed to stop taking the drugs. He should go natural and if pain persisted, he should get a medical checkup. A month later, after he cut out the steroids, he was training vigorously, running daily, and looking better than ever. He had regained his vitality, and once again life was a rewarding adventure.

Stress

Pressures at the office or at home can put a real damper on your energy levels. You have to find an outlet to lower your stress level, or your muscle gains will slow down or stop.

Making money can be fun. But don't get so absorbed with it that it cuts into your workouts and joy of living. If your job becomes drudgery, then take steps to change things in the workplace or find another one.

I remember talking to Arnold Schwarzenegger years ago about his life-style. He was quite content to get to the gym at ten in the morning, train for an hour and a half, saunter over to Zukky's on Wilshire Boulevard for lunch, and then lie around on the beach, napping on and off throughout the afternoon. He was adamantly against tying himself down with additional work that interfered with his easygoing life-style. But success breeds a need for more of the same. Today Arnold hardly has a minute to relax. His workaholic life-style has taken over.

And then there's Joe Weider. He told me the other day, "I'd give anything to be able to work out regularly. But I just can't find the time!" Can you imagine? The man grosses all that money every year and he can't find an hour a day for the thing he loves most.

Bill Pearl has the right idea. He takes care of his workout first thing in the morning. He says, "After that, I can devote myself to business without worrying about fitting my workout in at the end of the day."

Stress, wherever it comes from, is an energy killer. Try to keep your life organized and free of tension.

12

BODYBUILDING NUTRITION
Food for Growth

The most muscular are in town! Francis Benfatto (left) and Lee LaBrada get down to it.

The phenomenal Bob Paris—author, athlete, and role-model bodybuilder

I could go on about the importance of carefully balancing your nutrition into exact percentages, combinations, and calorie estimations all to help you achieve the perfect physique, but I do not believe in applying mathematics to a diet, especially in the off-season.

Mr. World, Dave Draper, told a group of enthusiasts recently at the World Gym in California: "As in life and in training, instinct also proves to be more reliable for diet than popular opinion or forced reasoning, and it is instinct that has given me a most sound diet philosophy—one rooted in balance and simplicity.

"Looking at today's bodybuilders, I notice great efforts being expended to maintain strict intake ratios of carbohydrates to protein to fat. Of course, while the process works for them, I don't feel that such a meticulously scientific approach is the most important aspect of a dietary regimen. I believe that a well-balanced diet and good supplementation can be realized instinctively."

I agree with Draper. Stay in touch with your body. By all means, read articles on bodybuilding nutrition, but don't worry about scientific proportions, numbers, and quantities in the calculations of protein, carbohydrate, and fat intake. There may be a case for getting out your calculator when ripping up your body for contests, but that's another chapter.

General Pointers

Don't miss breakfasts. Whether you're aiming to build up or rip up, breakfast is important. It's unwise to start the day by immediately getting on the road to work or school without a simple, nutritious breakfast. You can't manage properly through the day, let alone your workout, on a coffee and doughnut!

Nutritionists at the Food and Drug Administration agree that cooking causes some loss of nutrients. For example, cooking beef substantially reduces its thiamine, potassium, and niacin, and vitamins B_6 and B_{12}. Similarly, a high percentage of nutrients is lost in cooked fruits and vegetables. Whereas some people enjoy eating raw fish and meat, I don't want to promote

Marjo Selin has minimal fat and optimal muscle.

Cory Everson inspires the crowd every time.

such an undertaking. However, fruits and vegetables for the most part should be eaten raw wherever possible. Other foods should be grilled, broiled, or steamed just until they are done.

Base your entire food intake around fresh fruits and vegetables, lean meats, poultry, fish, eggs, milk, whole grains, and nuts.

Avoid adding salt or sugar to anything. Cut excess fat off all animal products. All dairy products should be low-fat items such as low-fat yogurt, cottage cheese, and skimmed milk. Cut down on the amount of egg yolks you eat; the egg white is low-fat high protein. Avoid highly spiced food and food with lots of additives.

Avoid high-sugar/high-fat desserts. There are many other delicious foods available that are much better for you. Rather than ice cream, canned, syrupy fruits, pies, and cakes, try a fresh fruit salad or low-fat yogurt.

If you're not in training for a contest or are trying to gain weight, raise your consumption of milk and milk products. Eat more red meat and eggs, but still maintain a balanced diet that is high in fruits and vegetables. Red meat does contain a significant amount of fat, as do whole milk and cheese. If you start gaining body fat, reduce your red meat consumption to every other day and eat only one egg yolk per two or three eggs. Eat low-fat cottage cheese instead of whole-milk cheese, etc.

During the off-season, a time when you should not be worrying about carrying a little excess weight, make sure that you include a high-protein food at every meal. During the sixties, bodybuilders tried to eat *only* protein—no carbohydrate—and frequently took in 400 to 500 grams of protein per day. While this has proven to be an unhealthy practice, it is still a good idea to include a high-protein food in every meal. High-protein foods include milk, eggs, meat, poultry, fish, cheese, yogurt, and nuts.

Let's look at a few off-season eating patterns of some champions. Of course, your particular dietary needs will probably vary from the samples shown here. However, I believe that when we analyze other bodybuilders' eating habits, we can learn from them.

Off-Season Eating Plans

Lee LaBrada

Breakfast
6 egg whites
1 cup oatmeal with low-fat milk, banana, and raisins
Bagel with low-sugar strawberry jelly
Supplements: multi-minerals, vitamin B-complex, C and E

Midmorning Snack
1 cup low-fat cottage cheese
Fruit
Bagel

Lunch
Tuna fish on whole-wheat toast
Baked potato (or rice or pasta)
Iced tea

**Midafternoon Snack
(two hours before workout)**
Oatmeal
Fruit
Baby food
Supplements: amino acids, inosine, gamma-oryzonol, and vitamin B$_6$

**Supper
(after workout)**
Chicken breast or fish
8 ounces lean flank steak
Steamed vegetables
Baked potato or yams

Snacks
Granola
Dried papaya
Protein drink
Daily total: 3,500 calories (25 percent protein, 65 percent carbohydrate, 10 percent fat)

Cory Everson

Breakfast
Oatmeal
6 eggs (only 3 yolks)
Protein drink (100 percent egg whites)

Midmorning Snack
Fruit
Protein drink (100 percent egg whites)

Lunch
Tuna salad
Bagel

Supper
Tuna salad or chicken

Evening Snack
Oatmeal

Bob Paris

Meal 1
Oatmeal (or other hot cereal)
2–3 ounces nonfat milk
Raisins
Fruit (banana, apple, peach)
1 whole egg, 3–4 egg whites (scrambled)
Coffee or tea

Meal 2
6–8 ounces chicken breast or broiled round steak (no higher than 7 percent fat)
2 cups rice (brown or white)
Vegetables (peas, corn, mushrooms)

Meal 3
2–3 pieces fruit (bananas, oranges, apples)
½ cup nonfat yogurt

Meal 4
6–8 ounces lean beef, chicken, or turkey
4 ounces pasta with tomato sauce
Salad (lettuce, carrots, celery, tomatoes, cucumber)
Lemon juice or limited amount of low-calorie dressing

Meal 5
2 pieces whole-grain bread
4–6 ounces lean meat
Lettuce and tomato

Bev Francis

Breakfast
Oatmeal with raisins, honey, wheat germ, and ¼ cup nonfat milk
3 egg whites, 1 yolk scrambled (sometimes with cheese)
2 slices whole-wheat toast with jam
Coffee

Midmorning Snack
Banana
Coffee

Lunch
Stir-fried chicken
Mixed vegetables
Steamed rice
Homemade bran muffin
Coffee

Midafternoon Snack
Protein drink (nonfat milk or juice, protein powder, berries)

Supper
10 ounces fish or (6 ounces steak)
Baked potato
Steamed vegetables
Sugar-free Jell-o with cooked peaches or apples
Coffee

Evening Snack
Toasted bagel with honey or jam
Hot chocolate

Vince Comerford

6:00 A.M.
2 jars baby food or 2 bananas
⅔ cup oatmeal with cinnamon

10:30 A.M.
8 ounces steamed chicken breast
8 ounces steamed broccoli
1 cup brown or white rice

2:00 P.M.
2 cups brown or white rice
Banana or some oatmeal

7:00 P.M.
12–16 ounces grilled halibut
6–8 ounces steamed vegetables
Green salad

Mike Quinn

Meal 1
10 egg whites
Oatmeal
½ melon

Meal 2
½ pound skinned broiled chicken
2 large baked potatoes
Steamed vegetables

Meal 3
½ pound fresh fish, such as swordfish
1 cup brown rice
Steamed vegetables

Meal 4
Broiled fish (or flank steak every third day)
Pasta
Steamed vegetables

Meal 5
½ pound skinned broiled chicken
Steamed vegetables

Tom Platz

8:00 A.M.
Cheese omelette
2 slices whole-grain bread
Milk
Supplements

10:30 A.M.
Tuna salad
2 slices whole-grain bread
1 slice hard cheese
Fruit juice

1:00 P.M.
Broiled chicken
Rice
Salad
Iced tea
Supplements

3:30 P.M.
Protein drink
Supplements

6:00 P.M.
Broiled steak
Baked potato
Green vegetable
Milk
Supplements

8:30 P.M.
Sliced meat
2 slices whole-grain bread
Yogurt
Raw nuts and seeds
Milk

Aaron Baker (left) and Van Smith

The ever-popular Bill Pearl with Janet Tech.

Pre-Contest Dieting

This is a time when you have to reduce your calorie intake to decrease your percentage of body fat so that by the date of your contest, your muscles show up in the most impressive way possible. Most bodybuilders weigh 10 to 20 pounds more during the off-season period, when they aren't preparing to enter a contest.

Getting started on a pre-contest diet can be tricky. The best way is to start slowly. Begin by just reducing calories by a few hundred a day. Never suddenly drop your caloric intake by a third or a half. Drastic changes like that will more than likely shock your body and disturb your metabolism, and they could well invite severe headaches.

Ironically, when bodybuilding contests first started, there was absolutely no pre-contest preparation. It wasn't until contests became annual events that bodybuilders began to think about preparing for competition. At first, this preparation took the form of an increase in workout length and intensity levels.

How things have changed. Today, getting ready for a contest has become a science. As far as training is concerned, intensity levels are increased as well as the overall number of repetitions per set. Some bodybuilders try to lessen the amount of rest time between sets. As the contest approaches, actual workout frequency may be increased. Instead of working each body part twice a week, a bodybuilder may opt to train each area three times weekly.

Nevertheless, restricting your eating plan to reduce body fat and bring out muscle definition is the real key to cutting up the body. In fact, some very successful bodybuilders don't change anything about their workouts; all their changes are related to their diets. Of course, it depends on how overweight you are, but most bodybuilders start their contest diet 8 to 16 weeks before a competition. A lucky few only have to diet for 4 to 6 weeks. As I have said before, the secret is to begin your diet in moderation. *Start by gradually reducing your food intake each week.* If you cut your eating plan too drastically, you will lose as much muscle as fat, and your workouts will be a constant fight against fatigue.

The following plan is a typical pre-contest diet. The portions, of course, will depend on your basic size and individual needs, and on the amount of fat you have to lose to obtain that contest-ready ripped physique.

Pre-Contest Diets

Breakfast
Bran cereal with nonfat milk and fruit
Egg-white omelet
Coffee, tea, or water (no sugar or cream)
Supplements

Lunch
Broiled fish
Green vegetable
Baked potato (no butter or sour cream)
Fresh fruit
Coffee, tea, or water (no sugar or cream)

Dinner
Broiled skinned chicken breast
Brown rice
Green vegetable or salad (with lemon juice)
Coffee, tea, or water (no sugar or cream)

Snacks
Turkey cold cuts
Raw vegetables
Apple slices

*   *   *

As the contest date gets even closer, this diet may have to be tightened up even more. It may look more like the following plan:

Breakfast
½ grapefruit (no sugar)
2–3 egg whites
1 slice whole-wheat bread (no butter)
Coffee, tea, or water (no sugar or cream)

Midmorning Snack
3½ ounces water-packed tuna
Radishes, celery, cucumber

Lunch
Turkey breast (no skin)
Lettuce, broccoli, zucchini (no dressing)

Midafternoon Snack
Raw vegetables
2 egg whites

Dinner
Broiled white fish
Spinach salad
Brown rice
Coffee, tea, or water (no sugar or cream)

Evening Snack
Apple
½ cup blackberries

This terrific gluteus tone belongs to Sandy Riddell.

As you continue your dieting, you should notice that your body fat is being reduced. After a few weeks, you may feel that you are looking worse. This is because when fat disappears, the skin doesn't always tighten up immediately. You may notice loose skin around your midsection or under the glutes. Don't lose faith. In time, your exercise and diet plans will come together and your loose skin will tighten up.

The most important fact about your ripping-up diet is that it is very low in fat. Fat makes you fat and eating less of it will make you lean. If you feel that you are losing it too quickly, then increase your portions slightly. But don't try to correct things by gorging on doughnuts or other sugar-loaded empty calories. All food that you eat during this period must be low in fat, salt, and sugar.

To avoid the metabolic "shut-down," never reduce your calories to less than 1,400 (for men) or 1,200 (for women). If you try to starve your body too severely, it will hoard calories and resist any weight loss. If you are not losing on a low-calorie diet, then increase your aerobic activity. Use a stair-climbing machine or stationary bike, or plan a walking or jogging routine.

The following are the pre-contest diets of Mike Quinn and Marjo Selin:

Mike Quinn

Meal 1
8–10 egg whites (cut out one week before show)
1 cup oatmeal
½ melon

Meal 2
½ pound halibut or sole
Baked potato
Steamed vegetables

Meal 3
½ pound broiled swordfish
Baked potato
Steamed vegetables

Meal 4
½ pound broiled fish or chicken
Steamed vegetables

Marjo Selin

Breakfast
Fresh fruit with a sprinkling of bran or oatmeal
Egg whites
Coffee, tea, or water (no sugar or cream)

Lunch
Broiled sole or halibut
Spinach or dark green vegetables
Baked potato (no butter or sour cream)
Fresh fruit
Coffee, tea, or water (no sugar or cream)

Dinner
Broiled skinned chicken or turkey breast
Brown rice
Salad (with lemon juice)
Coffee, tea, or water (no sugar or cream)

Snacks
Raw vegetables (carrots, celery, radishes)

The posedown: Samir Bannout, Mike Christian, Mohammed Benazizza, Gary Strydom, and Francis Benfatto get down to it.

Probably the most critical period of your contest diet is the last ten days before the event. This is make-it or break-it time. Try and make your competition weight a week before the show. As the seven-day countdown arrives, cut out all salt from your diet, including every food or drink that may contain salt. Read labels thoroughly. Don't eat processed foods or go to restaurants. Sodium holds up to 180 times its weight of water under the skin.

Perform your last workout three or four days prior to the show. By not training after that, your body will lose edema (water retention). During the last three days, the only exercise you should get is posing practice. Set aside two or three periods each day to practice your entire posing routine, including the relaxed stances and the compulsory poses—double biceps from front, side chest, double biceps from back, abdominals, and thighs.

If you have reached your contest weight (or less) a week before the show, you may want to hydrate yourself slightly. Take in small amounts of distilled water every two or three hours. During the last three days, watch your food intake carefully. Tailor it to your appearance every few hours. Cut out all salt (distilled water is your only fluid), and take a potassium supplement with your snacks. Your protein should come from brook or lake trout if possible. The best carbohydrates are fresh yellow corn and baked yams.

If you are determined to do your best at your first contest, practice your cutting-up procedure once or twice during the year so that you have some idea of how your body reacts to the process. Keep a diary at this time, recording all the details; then have photos taken of yourself so you can see how your body responds. This is also the time to experiment by taking supplements such as choline, inositol, niacin, vitamin C, and free-form amino acids. It's just not practical to guess how you will react to these so-called fat emulsifiers. Try a couple of dry runs and you will have a good idea of how to work things when your contest time arrives!

13

SUPPLEMENTS
Aids
for Bulking
Up

California's Aaron Baker

The biceps of Aaron Baker could stop traffic.

Recently I received a letter from a body-building nutritionist who approved of my "excellent training advice," but chided me for promoting the use of food supplements. The nutritionist wrote, "I really believe you know more about training than anybody else, Mr. Kennedy, but why don't you come clean with your readers over supplements? Why don't you tell the truth—that supplements are only food and do no more for building muscles than plain food?"

Why would I mislead my readers by telling them that supplements do nothing? I don't own any interest in companies that produce food supplements, so I have no products to sell. I have nothing to gain by either supporting or not supporting the case for supplementation. But, I believe that food supplements are important. You don't have to take them all the time, but you should take them to help achieve certain goals.

Larry Scott, a two-time Mr. Olympia whom I have never known to deliberately mislead anyone, categorically insists that he cannot gain size without supplementing his regular food intake with a high-quality milk-and-egg-protein powder. "And I don't just sip it out of a small glass," says Larry. "I mix up enough to make at least a couple of quarts so that I can really feed my muscles. I'll drink two or three glasses several times a day when trying to gain mass. It's the only way I can gain."

According to the Food and Nutrition Board of the National Academy of Sciences, diets of less than 1,800 to 2,000 calories a day *preclude getting adequate nutrition*. Therefore, people who are on 1,000- to 2,200-calorie diets are in danger of not getting their recommended daily allowances (RDAs) of certain nutrients. Ironically, most recommended diets are low-calorie diets in that range. Simply stated, dieters need supplementation.

Greg Zulak, formerly the editor of *Muscle-Mag International*, has done a great amount of experimenting with regard to supplements. "A quality milk-and-egg-protein mix, such as Beverly International or Natural Source Products, will do more for helping you gain pure mass than all the isolated aminos in the world," says

Zulak. And believe me, he has experimented with every imaginable concoction when it comes to musclebuilding supplements.

When you mix a milk-and-egg-protein powder, place the liquid in the container first, and then add enough powder to make a suitably thick but drinkable mix. You may add soft fruit (such as raspberries, blueberries, strawberries, peaches, or bananas). Most people use whole milk if they want to bulk up rapidly, but skim milk, water, or juice is recommended for those who may be inclined to add too much weight.

Amino Acids

Everybody wants to know just how good amino acids are. Most bodybuilders know the importance of ingesting protein for building muscle (after the water is removed from actual muscle cells, most of what's left is pure protein). They also know that proteins are made of various combinations of amino acids, which are the building blocks of the muscles.

The British nutritionist John Cortney explains it well: "When combined in the right proportions (since they are incomplete protein foods and supplements), amino acids form a peptide chain which is essential for protein synthesis to take place within the body." In other words, when you eat protein foods, your digestive system breaks the protein down into amino acids, and then re-forms them into protein that feeds your muscles.

Your body cannot manufacture a single molecule of this musclebuilding protein unless all the essential aminos are present at the site of protein synthesis. This leads to the question: What are essential amino acids? Amino acids are organic compounds found in all protein foods. Of the 22 amino acids, eight are categorized as essential and cannot be manufactured by the body. These eight essential amino acids are lysine, methionine, phenylalanine, valine, tryptophan, threonine, isoleucine, and leucine. Two other amino acids—arginine and histidine—are considered to be essential for pre-pubescent children, but not adults. The remaining amino acids are termed nonessential

Mike Quinn rips out a single-arm dumbbell row.

since they can be manufactured by the body, but they are nevertheless important nutritional elements to the aspiring bodybuilder.

There is no doubt that amino acids are vital for muscle mass development. Scientists have determined that the most easily metabolized amino acids are found in eggs, and when combined with milk protein, the overall value is improved further, producing the highest-possible protein-efficiency ratio.

Free-form amino acids taken as supplements are a useful aid to the bodybuilder. It is my experience that these supplements increase muscle mass and strength while at the same time reducing body fat levels. If this sounds too good to be true, let me qualify the statement. All these things occur but not in any mammoth proportion. They do not produce magical results, which is a claim made by the users of anabolic steroids. (But steroid abuse could threaten your health greatly.) Amino supplementation does give positive results, but considering the high cost of the free-form supplements, many consider the gain impractical. For this reason, as an off-season musclebuilding supplement, I recommend drinking a high-quality protein powder mixture. If you are preparing for a contest or a special photo shoot, then stop drinking the protein mixes and take some free-form amino acids. You may gain an edge that could well make a noticeable difference.

The muscles will only grow if the body is in an anabolic condition (hence, the frequent choice of anabolic steroids by so many bodybuilders). However, by combining certain free-form aminos, we can stimulate our own musclebuilding hormone in the form of hGH (human growth hormone), which is secreted by the anterior pituitary gland. (See Chapter 15 for more information about the human growth hormone.) Several free-form amino acids have been proven to stimulate hGH release, namely arginine, ornithine (an arginine derivative), cysteine, tryptophan, lysine, and histidine. Taken in conjunction with the performance of hardcore workouts, these amino acids will act to *safely* anabolize your system, creating the conditions for optimum muscle growth.

The Benefits of Supplements

One reason why supplements are necessary is that it's practically impossible to get them in their isolated form from regular food. Taking supplements enables you to tailor your dosages to your needs in a very precise way. Additionally, supplements enable you to combine different ingredients to achieve a variety of results. Supplements can be free of fat-building calories, and can be more easily digested than their equivalent in natural foods. Some supplements can supply energy and muscle food; others can raise the metabolism and help create the atmosphere for developing lean muscle mass. Which foods, for example, can give you the flushed effect to

bring out body vascularity like niacin? That in itself is reason enough to conclude that supplements are not *just* food. They are concentrates that can help you look bigger and better in a faster time than ever before.

Today in the bodybuilding world, we are constantly bombarded with "new" supersupplements that were either "originated by the Europeans," or discovered to be the "Russians' secret weapon" used to build their athletic prowess. Quite frankly, most bodybuilders can become confused, especially since these products vary in price from a few dollars to several hundred dollars for a 90-day supply. No one wants to waste money. On the other hand, no bodybuilder wants to miss out on getting the best nutritional help available. Let's examine some of the more popular supplements.

MCT Oils

Medium-chain triglycerides (MCTs) provide considerably more energy than carbohydrates and protein, and reportedly they are less likely to turn into body fat than long-chain fatty acids.

Twin Labs, which produces one type of MCT oil, claims: "Research . . . indicates muscle protein breakdown during catabolic states (such as prolonged, exhaustive exercise and dieting) where muscle breakdown exceeds muscle growth."

Some MCT oils may cause sickness if taken on an empty stomach or in excessive dosages. They have also caused digestion and assimilation problems. Be warned and check with your doctor if you have any adverse reactions when taking them.

Weight-Gain Powders

These are usually moderately high in protein and very high in calories. In fact, there seems to be a race as to who can manufacture the product with the highest calories per serving.

Make sure that the weight-gain product you use does not contain a lot of empty-calorie ingredients such as sugar. The main advantage of taking a weight-gain product is to obtain

Francis Benfatto

Canada's Negrita Jayde teases Samir Bannout.

Comparing relaxed poses—Mike Ashley (left) and Shawn Ray.

high-quality musclebuilding calories without overloading the stomach with additional meals. The best buys are: Champion Nutrition's Heavy Weight Gainer 900; Twin Labs' Gainer's Fuel, and Natural Source's Muscle Mass Gain Weight Formula.

Vitamin/Mineral Packs

You'll hear over and over again that no normal person following a healthy diet needs to go to the trouble and expense of taking vitamins and minerals. From the evidence, I am inclined to agree with this. However, a hard-training body-builder has highly specific needs. Weight training is a grueling activity. The aim is to develop muscle mass and strength. I believe that body-builders require more vitamins than the average person. So why not guarantee this by taking a daily vitamin/mineral supplement? It certainly won't do them any harm. Toxic effects from some vitamins only occur after prolonged and massive doses. I am particularly in favor of tak-

ing vitamins if you are dieting to lose body weight, or to cut up the physique for an upcoming contest. When you drastically limit your food intake, you definitely run the risk of depleting your nutritional needs. Taking a vitamin/mineral supplement would seem appropriate. The best buys are: Natural Source's Mega Multi-Vites, Beverly International's Daily Pack, and Hardcore's Mega Vitamin Pack.

I feel that although there are literally scores of supplements on the market for bodybuilders (many to increase energy, to improve performance, to accelerate recuperation, etc.), the most useful ones are those that induce the musclebuilding anabolic state (without, of course, producing the dangerous side effects of taking anabolic steroids). Nitrogen balance studies have shown that training bodybuilders require 1.67 times the established RDA for protein (0.8 grams/kilogram of body weight a day) to maintain lean body mass. Further studies revealed that a protein intake of 2.3 grams/kilogram of body weight a day resulted in greater muscle gains.

14

AMAZING GRACE

Muscles of Proportion

Tony Pearson

Samir Bannout gets serious with his incredible shape and proportion.

I can hear you hardcore bodybuilders now. "What are you talking about? Who cares about grace? We're into bodybuilding, not ballet dancing."

Well, give me the chance to tell you why I consider grace to be important: Grace is the opposite of ugliness and awkwardness. Now, I know you only want humongous mass. You want to break out of the pencil-neck mold. Believe me, building a herculean physique with squats, bench presses, and a high-calorie eating plan is not the way to impress anyone, whether you show off your body at the beach or on the competitive stage. To look good, a body needs more.

Don't misunderstand me—weight training is the most wonderful recreation in the world. It is the best single form of exercise. In fact, it's habit-forming (I've hardly missed a scheduled workout in thirty-five years). And the number of reasons for training with progressive-resistance exercise all your life is never ending.

But weight training can become static, especially if you limit the number of different exercises you perform. I am referring to the so-called abbreviated workout, where only basic exercises are used. To my mind, the human body is so complex and intricate that basic exercises alone do not bring out its muscle magic.

A number of years ago, I had arranged to photograph a top bodybuilder on a white Florida beach. This man was a former soccer player and hundred-yard sprint champion of his state. After going through his repertoire of poses, I made a few suggestions, all of which worked out well. Then, knowing of his athletic background, I told him that I would like a few shots of him running along the beach. Can you imagine my shock when after making several serious attempts, this Hercules Unchained had to admit he couldn't run? It was true. His best effort was no more than a slithering, fast walk. The man had done so many squats and so little of anything else that he had become incapable of running. That era of bodybuilding was during the earlier days when nearly everyone used steroids, and certainly no self-respecting bodybuilder of the day would run or even use a

Anja Langer is the epitome of scintillating form.

stationary bike for any kind of fitness or aerobic activity.

Nature has a way of making us good at only what we practice. Flexibility, muscle mass, agility, strength, and coordination only stay with us for as long as we perform the specific activities that promote them. We must practice not only to acquire, but also to maintain. The herculean bodybuilder on the Florida sands had ten years of heavy squatting behind him (he didn't even balance his legs by performing any leg curls), and in spite of being a former athlete, he had lost his running skill through complete neglect. And what's more, this tunnel-vision training had given him a blocky-looking physique: very heavy upper thighs, big, rounded, hanging pecs, and bunched-up shoulders. He had nothing graceful-looking about his body.

I'm not just talking about looking good for the opposite sex. Your shape and natural body grace will count just as much on the competitive stage. What do you think makes bodybuilders like Cory Everson, Francis Benfatto, Bob Paris, Mohamed Makkawy, Tonya Knight, Juliette Bergman, Anja Langer, and Serge Nubret all look so appealing? The appeal can be given several names: shape, line—or grace.

Admittedly, some people do have it naturally while others have to work for it. And many who have it naturally destroy it by poor training and nutritional practices. Getting fat is one of the quickest ways of losing your appeal. Fat fills in the valleys and crevices between the muscles, obscuring the distinct lines of your physique.

In the past, bodybuilding had some very powerful and big men and women. Some had enormous chests, legs, and arms, but who is remembered most? Champions like Frank Zane, Steve Reeves, and Rachel McLish. Why? Because they have the quality that few can put their finger on but seemingly everyone recognizes as being charismatic: physical grace.

Look at a typical male hardcore gym member. It's usually the men, not the women, who are the greatest offenders. What do you see? Heavyweight guys strutting around with awkward physiques and poor posture, that's what! Now if these men perform a front lat spread or front double biceps pose, they look pretty good. But what kind of a sight do they present when seen from the side? Awkward is the kindest word you can find to describe the vision.

Your body has to be built completely. If you just look good in a couple of poses, then you've got it wrong. Judges as well as other gym members, especially of the opposite sex, make a point of checking you out when you're not looking their way. In the gym, cursory glances are being thrown at you at an amazing rate. You're being checked out when you're training, lying on the beach, or just standing still. It never stops. It's the same when the judging panel is assessing competitors on stage. They don't just look at contestants when they are posing individually. A good judge will check out the various physiques from the minute the contestants walk on stage to the moment they leave. Seeing how gracefully a bodybuilder walks tells a judge a great deal about the individual's physique.

I will never forget seeing Bob Paris training at the World Gym in California. Right there, next to him, were many of the big names of the bodybuilding world. And compared to Bob Paris, most of them looked like Bart Simpson clones. Paris looked good from every angle, whether he was curling, pressing, squatting, or merely spotting his training partner. His posture and physique were virtually perfect. Multi-angle training builds this kind of form. Paris works with a large variety of exercises, does aerobics, and generally follows a holistic training style.

Here are some points to ponder so that you, too, can build form, line, and amazing grace into your physique.

Multi-Angle Training

You can't build a good physique with a handful of exercises; variety is what is needed. It's especially important to develop the rear deltoids, hamstrings, calves, forearms, lower thighs, lower abdominals, and lower biceps.

Performing a variety of weight-training exercises in itself is a positive move towards

Ming Chew uses an arm blaster to keep his curls in strict style.

building a well-proportioned physique, but the ideal way is to analyze your weaknesses and tailor your exercises to your individual needs.

Weight Control

Keeping your body-fat percentage at a moderately low level is vital. Men shouldn't allow themselves to add more than 15 pounds over their contest weight, and women should add no more than 10 pounds. Being overweight makes you not only look unattractive, but you have less self-esteem, feel sluggish, and even move with less elegance.

Aerobic Training

Bodybuilder Tina Plakinger says, "Aerobics build grace into male and female bodies." A body built exclusively from heavy weight training lacks cardiovascular fitness and health. Chunks of muscle alone project a weary message to the opposite sex.

Practice aerobics, not only to reduce your body fat levels and promote energy, but to maintain peak physical conditioning and grace of movement. Aerobic dance, rope jumping, stair climbing, and stationary and outdoor bicycling all have their place even for the most dyed-in-the-wool hardcore bodybuilder.

Laura Creavalle stretches it out for the judges.

Steroid Abuse

Steroid abuse definitely destroys your health and fitness. Not only will this abuse bunch up your shoulders, but there is a definite thickening of the midsection. In some cases, the waist becomes very bloated. Women develop an unattractive thickness in the obliques, upper gluteus, and lower abdominal areas.

Among other things, heavy steroid intake over a period of time will make you very stiff and prone to aches and pains. This will take away from your flexibility and mobility.

Non-Apparatus Exercises

Non-apparatus exercises will not build a Mr. Universe physique, but regularly performing them will give your body greater flexibility and increase your overall joint range of motion. You will appear more athletic. Include a variety of freestanding exercises such as wide-grip chin-ups, parallel bar dips, pull-ups, and floor dips with a diversity of hand placings.

Keep Perfect Posture

Your posture tells a great deal about your physical condition, prowess, and mental attitude. Some people have naturally erect posture typified by a flat back, tight abdomen, and square shoulders, while others find it a constant battle to stand or sit straight.

If good posture eludes you, make a point to practice keeping your back straight. Always walk with your shoulders held back and your head erect. When at work, straighten up your back, even when you're sitting. Write, type, eat, and talk with good physical bearing. In time, you will grow into your habit and good posture will become second nature to you.

Stay Active in Sports

During a concentrated bulking phase, it is acceptable that the individual not indulge in other physical activities or sports. However, you cannot remain inactive forever. Keep in touch with your abilities and skills in other sports that you enjoy. Did you excel in gymnastics at school or in swimming or diving? Maintain these skills while you continue your bodybuilding career. Your physique will look all the better for it. Few people know that Arnold Schwarzenegger thoroughly enjoyed scuba diving, swimming, archery, and skiing throughout his successful bodybuilding career.

Stretching

You'd be surprised at how many bodybuilders never stretch. It's vital to maintain your joint flexibility with regular stretching. As you grow older, you may find that your body tightens up more easily. Tendons and ligaments shorten and become less limber if they are seldom put to the test. Right now you may not even be able to put your hands flat on the floor while keeping your knees locked. You may not be able to even touch your fingertips to the floor!

The point is that if your joints and muscles are stretched out regularly, you will keep your body flexible and young-looking. Stretch for five minutes before and after your regular workouts. Stretching will help you to avoid injury. And it also improves athletic performance and contributes to a vital-looking physique.

New Apparatus and Exercise Machines

Free weights are still number one when it comes to your workout routines, but every month a new type of apparatus is invented. If new machines are installed in your gym, give them a try. There are some pretty nifty inventions out there, all of which can put a little extra edge and tone into that body of yours. After all, every little bit helps.

Masculine grace is exemplified by Shawn Ray.

15.
HUMAN
GROWTH
HORMONE
Stimulating Its Release

WBF pro Gary Strydom trains on a split routine more than once a day to maximize mass.

Human growth hormone (hGH) is synthesized in the anterior pituitary gland, which lies at the base of the brain and is less than one centimeter in diameter and weighs less than half a gram. Bodybuilders who are interested in muscle growth, especially natural growth that doesn't involve taking anabolic steroids, want to know how they can get their bodies to release growth hormone to increase muscle mass.

Dr. Frederick C. Hatfield says, "Some scientists tell us that there is no solid evidence that stimulating hGH release in any way, shape, or form is going to help bodybuilders and other athletes get bigger or stronger." This evidence is hotly disputed by biomedical research scientists Durk Pearson and Sandy Shaw. They quote two sources whose research has concluded that growth hormone increases a person's muscle-to-fat ratio. Also, Dr. Hatfield himself frequently recommends ways of stimulating hGH release in the body, so he obviously believes in its usefulness for bodybuilders.

Some bodybuilders, especially those who compete in advanced competitions, actually take a synthetic growth hormone, but this practice could be very dangerous. Taking excessive amounts could prove toxic to the body, and could even cause a serious disease called acromegaly, which is typified by a protruding forehead (making eyes look more sunken), unnaturally long elbows, and a heavy jaw. Even the hands and feet could enlarge. In rare cases of individuals who have not taken synthetic growth hormones but who have been known to suffer from acromegaly, the condition is usually caused by a malfunctioning pituitary gland that chronically releases too much growth hormone. If the condition is untreated, giantism can result where the individual grows to seven feet in height or more and develops a huge head and enlarged hands and feet. For the purpose of this chapter, let's confine the discussion to increasing growth hormone release naturally in the body.

Some researchers contend that the nervous system can be stimulated to release hGH. The hypothalamus is the receptor of this information, which in turn directs the pituitary gland to release hGH. Naturally bodybuilders want to know the factors that cause growth hormone production in the body and how much of it is ideal to maximize the effect. Little research has been done on humans, but Swedish scientists experimenting on rats showed that nine peaks produced the greatest growth. The release of more than nine peaks indicated a lessening of the effect.

How can you stimulate hGH release? First of all, you should realize that just as there are methods of creating an environment favorable to releasing the hormone naturally, you can also inhibit its release by incorrect actions. Let's examine some of these factors.

Training

Experiments with people involved in regular exercise have shown that medium- or low-intensity workouts that are drawn out in length, not only deplete the body generally, but also serve to inhibit growth hormone production. To maximize the likelihood of increasing growth hormone production, train two or three times daily in short, intense bursts. This may not be practical if you work or attend school on a full-time basis, but I would be giving you less than the facts if I didn't pass on the information. Incidentally, this philosophy of training would appear to be borne out by bodybuilders such as Arnold Schwarzenegger, Mike Christian, Gary Strydom, Tom Platz, and scores of other pros who train on a split routine more than once per day. Veteran trainer Vince Gironda himself, who is avidly against taking anabolic steroids, encouraged his pupil Mohamed Makkawy to train three times a day while preparing for the IFBB grand circuit.

Nutrition

In Chapter 12 of this book, Bodybuilding Nutrition, I recommend that whether you are trying to lose weight or gain weight, it is far better to eat five or six small meals a day than to eat the traditional three square meals of larger portions.

According to Dr. Hatfield, who is one of the few people conducting research regarding growth hormone release, "Some scientists concur that eating more frequent meals is a great way to stimulate hGH responses." Plan small, highly nutritious meals throughout your day if you want to make possible that extra progress.

Sleep

Few of us sleep more than once every 24 hours. However, scientists have evidence to show that every time we fall asleep for more than an hour, growth hormone is released into the body. Somatocrinin is released during sound sleep, and this causes an hGH response. Interrupted or restless sleep at night, however, can become a growth hormone inhibitor. Before retiring at night, attempt to clear your mind of problems by relaxing or reading until you feel sleepy. Your bed should be firm and comfortable. Make sure your bedroom is ventilated so it isn't too warm or stuffy. You need totally relaxed sleep time. Tossing and turning and allowing your mind to mull over problems will do nothing for your bodybuilding aspirations.

Sunshine and Saunas

While recognizing that sunbathing today carries its own risks of skin damage and possibly skin cancer, there is evidence to show that hGH can be stimulated by these natural heat rays.

Recently, growth hormone has been reported to be released in people who regularly spend time in saunas. In contrast, exposing the body to severe cold has shown itself to be an hGH inhibitor.

Amino Acids

High-quality amino acids (such as those manufactured by Twin Labs, Beverly International, and Hardcore Supplements) are believed to be involved in hGH release. Science hasn't quite zeroed in on all the facts yet, but there has already been enough evidence to show that there is a relationship between hGH production

Lenda Murray looks superfirm doing a cable curl.

and amino acid supplementation. In the near future, we will discover the results of numerous scientific experiments currently being undertaken to find which aminos do the best job. The present findings indicate that arginine and ornithine and niacin (vitamin B_3 in a 200-milligram dose) are most effective in their role of stimulating hormone production.

Keep subscribing to *MuscleMag International*, the bodybuilding magazine that is committed to publishing all new data on the subject of growth hormones.

Hardcore bodybuilders need all the help they can get to increase muscle mass. Until we have the full results of the current research, it is recommended that you perform regular workouts, get adequate rest, and follow a nutritious meal plan.

16

BODYBUILDING AND AGING

Training over a Lifetime

Diana Dennis

D r. Michael Colgan of the Colgan Institute in Encinitas, California, says, "You don't die of old age. You die of injury or disease. Science has not uncovered a single disease caused solely by time. The shaky hand, the wobbly leg, and the failing heart are end results of the way of life we lead. They can all be avoided."

Bodybuilding has been very popular now for over sixty years. In fact, it's safe to say that most males perform workouts with weights to build muscles at one time or another. This effort to improve physically may have only lasted for a handful of workouts, or it may have been a regimen followed for years or even a lifetime. Suffice it to say, we have all felt the need to work out to develop or trim our physiques and improve our health.

Whether you are still young or not is a question only you can answer. But regardless of your current age, it is vital that you realize the beneficial role of exercise as you grow older. It can help keep you feeling younger and stronger right into your golden years.

In the past, people didn't age well at all—they simply died young. According to statistics back in Abraham Lincoln's time, the average American could expect to live to 39. Today the average life expectancy is 75. The originator of *Iron Man* magazine, Peary Rader, says, "Barring accidents and plain ill fortune, to die before you are eighty is a waste of human resources."

What our society calls aging is really an onslaught of simultaneous attacks on the body by the environment, the food we eat, and the lifestyle we lead. And this attack begins in the womb before we are born, especially if our mothers smoked, drank alcohol, or ate junk foods. Even immediately after birth, our milk supply is tainted. Dr. Colgan says, "Pollutants such as DDT enter the infant's system in the mother's milk and also begin organ damage. This damage occurs mainly by oxidation. Mother's milk in America is now so polluted that it would be illegal to carry it across state lines in any other container."

Just because we age chronologically doesn't mean we have to age biologically—at

Danny Padilla looks great at 40 years old.

least not to the extent that we become weak, stiff, or physically incapable. Time itself is not the enemy. Degeneration is caused by damage and disease. Most of us can bring about a profound extension of vital life if we exercise, stop worrying, learn to relax, and eat correctly. In this way, we can keep our blood pressure and cholesterol level normal. Both reduce the probability of heart disease and diabetes—two of our most frequent killers.

Right now you should gear your training and nutrition programs to a long and healthy life, because time goes by second by second, week by week, year by year. You will realize this more and more as you get older. Time stops for no man. It doesn't just fly by. It sweeps over our heads from one horizon to the other like a lightning bolt!

To what age can we hope to make musclebuilding gains? Bodybuilders typically reach their peak in their twenties and thirties, but improvement can continue into the late forties. This is not to say that you can't take up training in your sixties and still gain muscles, power, and fitness. Scientific studies have shown that properly supervised training can increase strength, fitness, and cardiovascular condition even in 90-year-olds. Moreover, there have also been studies to show that former athletes who give up training in their teens or early twenties do not live longer than non-athletes. If you want to live longer, you should keep exercising. There is no longer any doubt that just being sedentary is a major risk for heart disease, whether you have exercised in your youth or not.

Fitness and bodybuilding writer Armand Tanny, who was also a former Mr. U.S.A., declares, "Exercise helps regulate blood pressure and metabolism, helps prevent loss of bone mass, lowers the concentration of artery-clogging fatty substances in the blood, and gives a higher self-esteem. The depression that often goes with retirement may be offset by regular exercise. Exercise at whatever age improves quality of life."

The Rules of Optimal Health

Older people who want to continue improving their health and fitness well into their forties, fifties, and sixties (and beyond) should follow these rules:

1. Base your diet around whole grains, vegetables, poultry, fish, and fresh fruits. Take a regular vitamin supplement if you are limiting your calories to lose weight.
2. Sleep an average of seven to eight hours nightly. Generally, five hours is too little; ten hours or more is too much.
3. Reduce your level of mental stress. Excessive worrying over family, financial, or work-related problems will cause anxiety-related heart or stomach conditions.
4. Always start your workout with a moderate amount of aerobic activity to get the heart and lungs pumping strongly.
5. Warm up with at least one set of "light" exercises with each new movement. For example, before doing ten reps in the press-behind-neck movement with 120 pounds, warm up with a set of 70 pounds (and maybe even a second warm-up set with 90 pounds).
6. Don't employ the heavy-duty method of training (all-out intensity). Excessive strain is not good for older trainers. Keep to moderate weights. By all means push yourself, but not to the extent of applying 200 percent to your workouts.
7. After even short layoffs, older trainers must start back with caution. Start with one superlight set of every exercise at the beginning. Your strength and condition will return quickly, but your first workouts must be light. Otherwise, you will overtrain and suffer headaches, diarrhea, or stomach upset.
8. Stretch before and after every workout. Stretch your hamstrings to their reasonable limit and stretch your back in all directions with nonballistic movements. Bring your knees to your chest while lying on your back. Perform reverse sit-ups; then try reverse trunk tilts and back raises.
9. Always train with a full range of motion to increase flexibility. Younger bodybuilders invariably use short-range maximum-intensity work that's the main trend in bodybuilding. But this should not be continued into the older years, since it will invite greater deterioration of the skeletal and muscular systems.
10. Limit your consumption of fried and junk foods. Drink alcohol only occasionally. Never take drugs or smoke tobacco. These latter two habits are lethal.
11. Keep a positive attitude. There are 30-year-olds who look and feel old, and there are 70-year-olds who act and feel young. It's a matter of attitude. The choice is yours.

Dr. Victor Katch confirms my remarks. "If you follow proper training principles, there's no question that muscles will continue to hypertrophy even into old age, but care has to be taken to follow sensible training procedures."

17
POSING FOR PICTURES
Physique
Photography

Not many bodies photograph as well as Francis Benfatto's.

Body building photography isn't just about holding a camera and pressing a button. As the publisher of *MuscleMag International*, I see many thousands of bodybuilding photos of men and women. Throughout the day, I am analyzing photographs and transparencies from all the best-known photographers. I also get to see work from the not so well known, as well as some downright awful stuff! I could certainly tell you who takes the best photos and who takes the worst.

What makes a great photograph? Well, there are no rules that cannot be broken, especially by the seasoned professional. It isn't even entirely accurate to insist that a great photo be completely in focus or that exposure should be perfectly measured. I've seen many out-of-focus photos that were over- or underexposed, but still masterpieces in their own right.

But guidelines certainly exist. A great picture should contain at least a high percentage of technical excellence. Sharp focus and correct *f*-stop settings are pretty rudimentary. Other considerations for great bodybuilding photos are that the subjects have life and vitality. The photo must say something. This effect can be brought about by posing the subject selectively. A picture must carry interest—it must have soul, color, and impact!

Not long ago Ben Weider, the president of the International Federation of Bodybuilders (IFBB) phoned me. He said, "How would you like to meet Ivan Lendl? I'm presenting him with an IFBB medal at the Skydome in Toronto. Can you meet me at the airport?"

I agreed. Of course, I knew all along that the reason I was being invited was to take a photograph of the medal presentation. Ben's plan was not just to honor Ivan Lendl as one of the world's hardest-training athletes, a person whom he genuinely admired, but to also publicize the existence of the IFBB. He wanted the pictures to go to the news syndication networks. However, if he was photographed merely shaking hands or standing next to Lendl, none of the news agencies would bother to send the picture out to the world's press. But if Ben could hold the tennis champ's arm above his head in a victory stance, then the photo would have some greater significance, and it would indeed be circulated to the newspapers around the globe.

In the press room, Ben Weider made a very eloquent speech. Lendl appeared to be pleased, and at the conclusion, Ben closed in on the tennis player and presented him with an engraved plaque. My camera was at the ready. I observed Ben's right hand creeping toward Lendl's left wrist. Quick as lightning, he made the grab, hoisted Lendl's arm skyward, and smiled at my lens. Click! I got the shot. It had impact and was seen in newspapers around the world.

Looking Your Best in Photos

When you have your picture taken, you cannot expect the photographer to perform a miracle. Even the best photographers cannot make you look ripped to shreds when you have the smoothness of a wet seal. You have certain responsibilities and steps you can take to be at your best.

1. You must be in shape. The great photographer Russ Warner says, "Even if you don't enter contests, prepare yourself as if you were. Get in the best shape of your life, because the photo session is a big event!"
2. You must be tan all over—especially important are the sides of your legs and under your arms. A patchy, uneven tan will spoil every picture. Get some sun naturally, add a bit of artificial coloring, or go to a tanning salon. Many bodybuilders do all three. If you have any unsightly blemishes, use a cosmetic preparation to cover them up.
3. Pay attention to the color and cut of your posing outfit. Fashions change, so check out what the top bodybuilders of the day are wearing. A glance at *Muscle & Fitness*, *Flex*, or *MuscleMag International* will give you some ideas. If you're dark-skinned, you

Krista Anderson and Garry Leonard pose for Steve Douglas's camera for a *MuscleMag* cover.

might like to wear bright colors such as red, purple, lime green, or orange. Lighter-skinned individuals may prefer light blue or sea-green. Black or white outfits are not favored by magazine publishers. They are looking for bright colors to add splash to their periodicals.

4. Be well groomed. This is important. You cannot turn up at a photo session un-shaven with unkempt hair and generally looking like an unmade bed. Be sure your finger and toenails are cut and clean. Men should shave off excess hair on the body and under the arms.

5. Make sure you have control over your facial features. Practice your smile regularly. Learn how to increase the voltage in your eyes. Develop a closed-lip smile and an open-mouth smile. Also practice a serious

look. Not all of us can have the natural good looks of a James DeMelo, Bob Paris, or Steve Reeves, so work on being able to project the best face possible when it comes to the photo session.

6. Don't bring a bunch of friends to your photo session. Perhaps one friend is per-missible, but be sure that he or she isn't a would-be photographer. Your assistant can help with your preparations, but if you bring someone with a big mouth, you will jeopardize your relationship with the cameraman.

7. Arrive on time to a photo session. Body-builders are known for turning up late. If you want to be a success, get there on time. Once a multi–Ms. Olympia winner turned up four hours late for a photo session, and then without one word of apology,

Author Robert Kennedy with Gary Strydom and James DeMelo.

snapped, "Let's get this show on the road—I'm hungry!"

8. Get yourself up for the photo session. You cannot allow yourself to be in a gloomy mood when you are having your picture taken. You need to have a look of zest, virility, health, and vitality. You may not have slept much the night before. Perhaps you feel drained or ill-tempered. Maybe you are shy. Whatever the case, snap out of it. That camera is going to record your mood. Fake it the best way you know. You have to do everything possible to project a positive attitude.

9. By all means, make suggestions to the photographer if he lacks ideas. But if he is a true professional, he will give you directions. Don't fight him. Remember, there is a reason for everything you are asked to do. If you are told to suck in your waist more, it means your waist is looking too big. Leaning back a little may get the light to hit your abs just right. Twisting the arm a fraction would highlight the triceps muscle perfectly. Be patient with the photographer. You have to work together for best results. If you make him feel rushed, he'll lose interest in the photo session.

Some of the Best Photographers in the Business

Mike Neveux

He is co-owner of *Iron Man* magazine and is considered one of the most creative photographers in bodybuilding. Technically, Neveux is without peer when it comes to versatility. He can shoot action, exercise, posing, and contest pictures. He offers originality and can shoot in natural light or using a strobe with equal ability.

John Balik

John has moved over recently to allow Mike Neveux to do almost everything photographically for *Iron Man*. But like Neveux, he is a very competent, all-round photographer, not as technically perfect, but equally as good as Neveux when it comes to shooting bodybuilders at the correct angle.

Chris Lund

He is known as Mr. Focus. Chris delights in taking black-and-white hardcore images that capture the reality of strenuous bodybuilding training.

Bill Dobbins

By sheer will of effort, Bill Dobbins has mastered the art of bodybuilding photography. Now he is right up there with the best.

Ralph DeHaan

He is a consistently excellent photographer who is emerging as an industrious, creative bodybuilding cameraman. He is especially good at photographing women.

Steve Douglas

Steve is naturally a very creative and technically competent photographer. His main work is in the creative design department at *MuscleMag International* magazine, so he doesn't spend much of his time taking pictures. Photography is almost a sideline with him, but he's fast becoming known as one of the best in bodybuilding.

Russ Warner

The best bodybuilding photographer of yesteryear, Russ has taken the most memorable pictures of men from the fifties, such as Steve Reeves and Vince Gironda. Russ specialized in posed photographs with picturesque outdoor backgrounds. Now in his seventies, he's still taking bodybuilding photos in the San Francisco area.

Art Zeller

Don't mention strobe lighting or studio shots to this man. He is a natural-light photographer. He drives for hours to find an ideal location, and then takes his time to set up a single shot. But the results speak for themselves. Zeller is the only bodybuilding photographer whose work has depth of reality and total soul.

*   *   *

Of course, there are several other good photographers. Albert Busek from Germany, Per Bernal from Sweden, Lucien Demeilles from France, and Jim Amentler from the United States are all up there with the best when it comes to bodybuilding camera work.

Francis Benfatto's muscles are massive—look at his arms and shoulders and his amazing calf.

INDEX